There was just me, the kid and the plastic hose; surely the perfect opportunity to realize the fantasies that I had been enjoying after I had spotted him slyly peeping into our room when David and I had been taking a non-sleeping siesta. I got to my feet and, still wearing Eve's costume, walked to within a metre or two of him. He gazed at me as though he were hypnotized. I asked him, since it was a particularly hot day, to play the hose on me to cool me down a bit. I opened my legs and made it obvious that I wanted the full treatment . . .

XAVIERA HOLLANDER

Knights in the Garden of Spain

GRAFTON BOOKS

A Division of the Collins Publishing Group

LONDON GLASGOW
TORONTO SYDNEY AUCKLAND

Grafton Books
A Division of the Collins Publishing Group
8 Grafton Street, London W1X 3LA

A Grafton UK Paperback Original 1988

ISBN 0-586-07432-5

Printed and bound in Great Britain by
Collins, Glasgow

Set in Times

Contents

Prologue

I don't drink; I don't smoke. A girl has to do something and I had just finished doing it. I was languid and relaxed and felt happily at peace with the world. For its part, the world (or its sole representative who was with me in bed) seemed quite satisfied with me.

The night was warm and there was just the whisper of a breeze which ruffled the palm trees and set the rigging of the yachts outside the bedroom window gently tinkling. A restful, soothing sound. I stretched my legs and gently caressed the world's representative.

'Darling, find a smooth and sexy record to play me to sleep.'

He crossed the room and after a little thought selected a disc. I was already half asleep and the music was peaceful.

'That's nice,' I murmured. 'What is it?'

'"Nights in the Garden of Spain" by Manuel de Falla; a sort of piano concerto.'

I smiled as I remembered the passion of Pepe as we made love. Or was that Juan? I recollected the charm and courtesy of Antonio as I lay in his arms. Or perhaps that was Luis. Then there was Fernando with his huge cock. No, that must have been Jaime!

'Like a knight on horseback with his lance out-stretched,' I mused, smiling contentedly as I recalled my cavaliers and the perfumed evenings we had spent together.

'My Knights in the Garden of Spain,' I smiled as I drifted into sleep.

1

A Man Needs Remaking

Spain was waiting for me. I was looking forward to the sunshine, the white-walled towns and villages, nestling beside the sea, fiestas and flamenco. My mind kept turning to thoughts of Spanish men – dark, lithe, sunburned men with flashing eyes and strong limbs. Handsome, arrogant men! This was my first visit to Spain for many years and I was sure that it was going to be a memorable one. Franco had been dead for a year and I hoped to find a new atmosphere of sexual freedom and to enjoy it. I had crossed the Atlantic and swept through Europe; a new episode in my sexual odyssey was about to begin.

I had driven too fast in my new BMW to be able to examine the local flora or fauna and had not felt like stopping for sightseeing. I was in a restless frame of mind; I had left the United States and Canada but had not yet settled down in Europe. I was unhappy and searching for – I did not know what. Perhaps I would find the answer among those attractive Spanish men.

Marbella was quiet: the tourist season was not yet in full swing. I was to discover that near the end of July the world and his wife would arrive at half-past two one afternoon, apparently all climbing out of one Volkswagen. Now, at the end of May, the Old Town, a picturesque maze of lanes too narrow for motor traffic to negotiate with comfort, lined with shops for the unwary tourist, lay tranquil and lovely. On the other side of the main road was the other Marbella: fashionable boutiques and the tall towers of the new hotels, surrounded by their pools and gardens; the Marbella which was already challenging the smart resorts of the Côte d'Azur.

I had driven down with my mother and we checked into one of those elegant hotels, clean, comfortable but not ridiculously fashionable. We were tired and decided to take it easy for the first night.

Next day we went to the beach and I inspected what the locals had to offer. In the morning sunlight, groups of bikini-clad girls stretched their bodies on the sand, attracting the attention of the caballeros who paraded their bodies and their fancy bathing trunks before what they fondly imagined to be admiring throngs. My mother lay on a beach mattress, watching me anxiously. She hoped that Xaviera was going to have a holiday, but my idea of a holiday was very different from hers. She was ready to protect her baby daughter from the wicked schemes of over-attentive males, but I reckoned that it was a little too late to fight to safeguard my virginity.

'Why don't you go and buy yourself an ice cream?' I invited.

As soon as her back was turned, I made the acquaintance of a handsome young man who had been eyeing me appraisingly. In his mid-twenties, not very tall but well built, he had an interesting face and soon we were discussing everything except the one subject which was on both our minds. I had so looked forward to my first encounter with a Don Juan that it was a bit of a disappointment that Hermann was an import from Stuttgart. Mother returned with her ice cream and I introduced Hermann. She seemed uneasy. Then I told her that we were meeting that evening for dinner and she was distinctly unhappy. However, the gentleman was very correct and polite and the tension eased. I saw more of Hermann for the next few nights, not always with Mother, and he proved to be a competent lover. He had already sampled several girls along the coast and he would surely not have won any award for constancy. We got on well enough, but I knew that he was not the magnet which had drawn me to Spain.

A few days later I was invited to meet a group of people for a drink at Menchu's, a fashionable bar in Puerto José Banus. The Port, as the place was always called, was a newly-built yacht basin surrounded by houses and apartments, boutiques and restaurants. It was very, very pretty; a picturesque, miniature town lying in the embrace of the sea and under the gaze of a majestic mountain. My host was Daniël, who had only recently arrived in Marbella himself, and had rented a large villa. He seemed to me to be an intriguing and rather exotic character. He was highly intelligent and viewed the world with the cynical detachment of the extremely wealthy. He appeared to enjoy spending money, so I had no compunction about accepting his invitation. I wondered what sort of characters would be in his entourage.

There we were, a dozen people, chatting and sipping drinks. The women tended to eye me suspiciously, but I was getting used to that sort of treatment from females who regarded me as a threat, particularly when they had a rich man in tow. Most of the males regarded me with obvious curiosity, but the small talk was very small indeed until we moved off to lunch.

My attention had been taken by a small, untidy man of about fifty and I took his arm as we walked to the restaurant. He was not the most handsome man in the company although the competition was not too intense, but he seemed to have more personality than the others. I learned that his name was David, that he too had only recently left Great Britain and that he was staying at

Daniël's villa. We took to each other immediately, and I soon realized that, like myself, David had left a great deal behind and had not yet grown new roots in Spain. We talked throughout lunch: he had a keen sense of humour which appealed to me and also a willingness to laugh at himself without embarrassment or false pride, and I warmed to him. I needed the company of an older man rather than the inexperienced, totally sex-absorbed teen-agers who congregated on the beach. We agreed to meet for dinner. God, I thought, first Hermann, now David, where are the handsome Spaniards of my dreams? So often, although I fantasized about young, strong, beauti-ful men, it was in middle-aged men of character and intelligence that I found true affection.

I had already decided that David needed a strong-minded woman to take him in hand, and I felt that this was something I really wanted to do. His dress sense was appalling and he had no interest in his appearance. His hair would have been quite nice if he had brushed it differently, and he walked as if he were looking for a coin which he had just dropped. David, I concluded, was clean but a mess! When he presented himself at my hotel that evening, he was washed and shaved but still dressed without the slightest regard for fashion.

We dined at a Japanese restaurant, recommended by the hall porter at my hotel, and I learned more about David over the meal. Suddenly, a bottle of champagne materialized, embarrassing since I do not drink, accom-panied by a card on which was written 'To The Happy Hooker for her honeymoon with the compliments of the management'. I thanked the manager profusely but he looked puzzled. David drank some of the wine and I lifted the glass to my lips. There was the sound of laughter from the ornamental garden outside the restaurant. There were

Daniël and the rest of our companions from lunch, watching us as if we were on a television screen: of course, they were responsible for the champagne.

Afterwards, things moved quickly. We all drove back to Daniël's villa and it seemed natural that I should stay the night with David. Daniël and his pretty young Moroccan wife, Joëlle, retired early and the only other guests that night at the villa were an Irish married couple, Paddy and Bridget, who viewed the world through a permanent alcoholic haze. Our bedroom was separated from theirs by a shared bathroom.

'Ever take a bath with a girlfriend?' I asked David.

He shook his head. I stepped into the tub and beckoned him.

'Come along in, the water's fine and I object to going to bed with smelly men. Besides, it's one of those things which are more fun done together.'

David looked much better without his clothes, and I was pleasantly surprised when I looked him over by the flickering light of a large candle. I have always liked the sight of a circumcised cock and David had a prick with personality. In the tub, it was a tight squeeze but an interesting fit, and as his firm body pressed against my soft flesh, I congratulated myself on my choice. I took his cock lovingly between my lips, but I had to take care that he did not come within a few seconds. It must have been a long time since he had last enjoyed this experience, but with a little guidance he found my clitoris and proved to be a fast and furious pupil. I delayed my first orgasm as long as I could to prolong the intense foreplay, but he sucked me with such enthusiasm that neither of us could hold back any longer and we came simultaneously. The amount of sperm which gushed into my mouth confirmed my impression that it had been quite a time since this man had been with a woman. Not that he was a sexual innocent: when, under my supervision, he massaged my tits with his long sensitive fingers, it was entirely his own idea to drop the soap and go exploring my ass in search of it.

It did not take him long to recuperate, and although I took credit for his renewed king-sized erection, I must admit that the raw material was pretty good. We slopped a hell of a lot of water out of the bath; there must have been more on the floor than in the tub. I climbed to my feet and pressed David's head against my belly; he licked my navel and I felt a delicious thrill run through my body. My greedy cunt closed around his fingers and his quiet gasp of pleasure merged with my shriller cries. All our muscles were taut and as our movements became more agitated, we slipped and slithered in the half-empty tub. But it was not only in the bath that we made waves. There came a plaintive tapping on the wall from Paddy's bedroom.

'Can't you be a bit quieter? Some people are trying to get some sleep.'

We giggled but quickly (and quietly) towelled each other and hurried to bed. But as I threw open the bathroom door, I saw Paddy in a short dressing gown, standing close to the door, obviously eavesdropping – a sort of aural voyeur.

'I thought that you wanted to go to sleep,' I challenged.

Paddy went very red. 'I was just going to get a glass of water,' he said.

I looked at him as if I did not believe him. David looked at him as if he did not believe him. Finally, Paddy looked at us as if he did not believe himself either. David had the last word.

'The kitchen is in the other direction,' he pointed out.

Back in our bedroom, we got down to serious business. I only had to touch his cock with my fingers or my mouth to feel that throbbing sensation go through me once more. David was teetering with anticipation when he finally plunged his shaft deep inside me. I could sense his relief, and gradually we speeded up our rhythm and again reached our orgasm together.

'Does that happen often?' David asked, when he had got his breath back.

'What?'

'Two in a row and both simultaneous.'

I shook my head. 'I guess that I am a healthy woman with a rather more than average appetite for sex. But it has a lot to do with feeling. I really like you a lot and that was not simply fucking; we put a lot of loving into that.'

Next morning, I explained to David that I had to go back to Mummy. I had brought her to Marbella where she knew nobody, so I could not leave her on her own all the time. When David arrived at the hotel, bearing the traditional peace offering of flowers which my mother duly accepted, they got along fine. He was so much nicer than Hermann, she assured me, a serious man, the sort of man with whom I ought to be settling down.

But the following day, it was with a puzzled and slightly shame-faced expression that my new lover greeted me.

'Xaviera, I have to talk to you seriously.'

Good God, he's not going to propose marriage, is he? I wondered.

'I woke up this morning with a problem,' David continued, 'and I'm afraid that it involves you.' With supreme English tact, he explained that he had a discharge from his penis, and since he had not slept with anybody else for months, he ventured to suggest that there might be some connection between his affliction and our night together.

My immediate reaction was – Oh, Christ, I've got the clap! Foolishly, I let my mother know that we were going together to find a doctor – and the reason. Her reaction was predictable; she wailed and she wept and she complained of the selfishness of her daughter who had infected so good a man. What I did not predict was that she would then storm off to the beach where she confonted Hermann and, in front of his current nymphet, accused him of having passed on his disease to me.

Meanwhile, David and I found Dr Jimenez; dark, young, earnest and about to leave for the weekend. He was reluctant to delay his departure, but we were desperate, and when David's back was turned I used the most direct method of persuasion. He was not very impressed by David's minor discharge.

'Could be anything,' he sniffed. 'Still, as you are here, there's no point in taking any chances. Whatever you have, this will kill it.'

He seized the largest hypodermic syringe I have ever seen and filled it with what seemed gallons of penicillin. I looked uneasily at the instrument of torture, and David turned several shades paler. With a deft jab, Dr Jimenez impaled the proffered buttock and slowly emptied the syringe. David did not have to tell me that it hurt; he limped for days. Then it was my turn.

'Isn't there some sort of test you could give me to tell if I need the treatment?' I implored.

'Yes,' he conceded. 'If you think it is worthwhile.'

I thought that it was very worthwhile and I was spared the immediate agony. We waited. Dr Jimenez concluded his analysis and returned.

'Neither of you has any form of infection,' he told us scornfully. 'You,' he addressed David, 'are suffering from a hormonal reaction usually due to resuming sexual

activity after prolonged abstention. I'll give you a preparation which will clear it up.'

My relief at not having to take that ghastly shot was
overwhelming, but I had the impression that David felt
that he had been swindled. But the person who took the
news worst was my mother. She could not believe that
Hermann was blameless, and it was left to me to convey
the glad tidings to him and apologize for Mummy's
outburst. He, of course, was horribly smug, the personifi-
cation of outraged innocence.

'I don't know how you could ever have suspected me,'
he proclaimed.

But the shock had affected me and for the rest of my
stay in Marbella I was completely faithful to David – well,
nearly.

2

Einstein? Rubinstein? Frankenstein?

Now that I was spending half of my days with David, I got to know Daniël's villa and its occupants better. Both Daniël and Joëlle were obsessed by games. They would compete against each other or any passing visitor with the ferocity of a brace of sabre-tooth tigers whose privacy had been disturbed by a flock of brash sheep. Not that they were guilty of physical violence: they confined themselves to using playing cards as weapons and chess or backgammon boards as battlefields. When they felt energetic, they would sit in the garden and regard their pool: the sight of the limpid blue water would completely satisfy their urge to indulge in exercise and they could concentrate on life's pressing problem – where to have lunch. I commented to David on the idyllic quality of life at the villa.

'It's like those interminable Russian novels where nothing happens for several hundred pages,' he growled. 'Bloody Chekhov in the sun!'

The household was run effectively by two local maids, both named Maria, and called consequently Maria Una and Maria Dos, but they were never sure themselves which was which. Presumably, the eight-months-pregnant one was Maria Dos. The other member of the staff was a decrepit gardener who moved slowly around, collecting twigs and dead leaves. After a few days, our hosts left for a trip to Switzerland, where Daniël kept his money, and Paris, where Joëlle spent it, leaving David and myself alone in the villa. This was a relief to me because I was now able to sunbathe and swim in the nude. Previously,

18

Joëlle had objected on the grounds that I would distract the staff. The maids were far too busy to notice and the gardener was too old to care. However, he did have a son in his early teens whose vocation in life appeared to be to carry a large, phallic hose about the place. I noticed that while I was allowing the sun to make the acquaintance of those parts of my body which had been previously hidden, the boy spent more and more of his time close to me, watering the grass as if he were intent on deluging the whole of Andalucia. As he manoeuvred nearer and nearer, the hose seemed to grow larger and larger.

One day, David had gone to Marbella on some errand and I had taken up my customary pitch beside the pool. The maids were somewhere out of the way and the aged gardener had pottered off, probably to drink himself into a stupor. There was just me, the kid and the plastic hose; surely the perfect opportunity to realize the fantasies that I had been enjoying after I had spotted him slyly peeping into our room when David and I had been taking a non-sleeping siesta. I got to my feet and, still wearing Eve's costume, walked to within a metre or two of him. He gazed at me as though he were hypnotized. I asked him, since it was a particularly hot day, to play the hose on me to cool me down a bit.

I opened my legs and made it obvious that I wanted the full treatment, from head to toe, including the hottest spots. He sprayed me, but avoided aiming directly at my crotch. I pointed at my triangle; the hose wavered for a moment, but he obeyed. There was a bulge forming under his shorts and, as I watched, it grew bigger until the top of his cock peeked out of one leg. It was such a turn-on that I almost had an orgasm there and then. I gestured to him to turn off the hose and come over to me. I grabbed him, ripped off his shorts and pushed him on to his back.

19

In the long, wet grass, with an army of ants crawling all over us, I overpowered the young Spaniard and virtually raped him. I climbed over his slender body; his prick looked larger than I had expected, perhaps because he had hardly any pubic hair. I soaked him with the water which was still streaming from me. Soon our perspiration had drenched both of us.

The boy fucked like an express train running behind schedule, and I tried slowing him down somewhat, but there was no way that I could get him to observe the signals: it was full speed right to the terminus. I had a terrific time, watching the passion in his beautiful, dark face on which there was the first suspicion of a moustache, and clasping his tight little buttocks as they bounced up and down. With every thrust, I pulled him closer until, quite suddenly, he uttered a loud shriek and came with one final rush.

He got up hurriedly, pulled on his trousers and looked around anxiously in case his father had shown up. Seeing that he was safe, he whispered '*muchas gracias*' in my ear, picked up his hose, walked to the other end of the garden and continued to water the plants as if nothing had happened.

When David got back, I gave him a detailed account of the episode. I wondered how he would react, but he was admirably cool, saying that he was well aware of my lifestyle and that he had not expected me to be more than relatively faithful. That was nice: from then on, we enjoyed a relationship of complete freedom and honesty and we got quite a kick from relating our adventures to each other.

That night, we were in bed when Daniël called from Zurich. It had to be something urgent and I was surprised when David passed me the phone.

'Listen, Xaviera, I have a problem.' Daniël sounded worried. 'I'm alone, but I have found this lovely, red-haired woman and she's prepared to come to bed with me, but not to stay the night. From your experience, what should be the rate for the job? She's asking five hundred.'

'Five hundred what?' I asked facetiously. 'Pesetas?'

'Dollars,' he replied indignantly. 'Don't you think that's a lot?'

'Be generous, it won't hurt you this once,' I advised, and hung up.

David was laughing his head off. My first thought was that the guy was a true john, a type who could only get his rocks off if he paid for it, but David said that I did not understand Daniël's brand of humour.

'He's had plenty of experience and did not need your advice,' David explained. 'He thought that we would be busy fucking, and hoped to disturb us, especially since our sex is on a non-commercial basis.'

During the next few days, unembarrassed by the presence of strangers, I got to work on remodelling my lover's image. I started in the pool. David could swim a leisurely breast stroke, as became an English gentleman. I taught him to crawl; after a few reluctant lessons, he could perform a passable imitation of a half-paralysed dog. As for diving, he was certain that leaping into the pool head first could fracture his head and leave him embedded in a deep hole in the bottom. But I persevered, and after a while he was no longer hitting the water stomach first. And with the exercise, he began to lose some weight and assume a more pleasing shape.

I remember vividly the night when I extended my course of instruction to the dance floor. We went to the Marbella Club, a fashionable hotel where the discotheque was patronized by a mixture of genuine aristocrats and the usual snob mob, all exquisitely dressed. I was wearing a long evening gown from Paris: my escort was less than splendid in a pair of faded, baggy yellow pants with bulging pockets. His appearance contrasted with the look of the smart, handsome men all around me: I certainly had a man for all seasons. After all, I was still in the summer of my life whereas he was in the autumn of his, although when we were together it did not make any difference. However, a more contemporary wardrobe and hairstyle would not do him any harm, and I devoted some time to tidying up my man, with some success.

Indeed, when Daniël was back with us and David walked in, resplendent in new tight-fitting jeans and a bright red shirt, our host, who was as shabby as befitted a millionaire, remarked: 'I do like your Peter Pan outfit: where did you get it?'

Both David and I had decided to find places to live near each other and he soon bought a charming and luxurious apartment in the Port, looking directly on to the sea. It was owned by Madeleine Carroll, a famous movie actress of the pre-war period. David admitted to me that she was the first woman with whom he had fallen in love: he had been seven at the time. When we met her, she must have been in her seventies, but she was still fascinatingly beautiful and radiated charm. Very slim and elegantly clothed in a yellow dress with long sleeves, she sat on the patio of her lovely house in the mountains and chatted to us of her days in Hollywood. Her make-up had been applied with exquisite taste, her face had the quality of delicate porcelain and her eyes were so blue that they appeared to be almost transparent. She was the perfect, gracious hostess and we sat, spellbound by her narrative.

I recall her account of her first encounter with that most eccentric of multi-millionaires, Howard Hughes.

'I was living in a superb bungalow on the beach while I worked on a film with Cary Grant. Coming home one evening, I was alarmed to find a man sprawled on the divan in my lounge. He got to his feet and explained that he was my neighbour and that he had broken in to borrow a Coke. It sounded an unlikely story and his appearance did nothing to give me confidence; a dirty shirt over even dirtier trousers and worn sneakers which had perhaps once been white. However, he did not seem to be dangerous and he took his Coke and departed. A few days later, the same thing happened again, but this time my uninvited guest introduced himself as Howard Hughes and invited me to dine with him the following Friday. I was surprised when he suggested that we meet, not at the restaurant, but at a busy street corner in town. However, Howard Hughes already had a reputation for his odd behaviour.

'I was excited and wondered what to expect. When I walked out of the studio that Friday wearing my finest evening gown, the gate-keeper asked me where my limousine was. I explained that I was meeting a friend outside, but I had lost status with him and he never acknowledged me again. After I had waited for a while at our unglamorous rendezvous, my date showed up, dressed in the same dirty shirt, dirty trousers and worn sneakers. He asked me where I would like to eat and, still in a state of shock, I left the choice to him. He led me to what was termed in Hollywood a greasy spoon. To be fair, there was an option of two spoons, hamburger or hot dog. I took a hot dog, but Howard Hughes was always adventurous and he had the hamburger. We split a bottle of Coke and the bill for this feast amounted to $1.50. My escort slapped down some coins on the table. "Great," he said, "here's my 75 cents, where's yours?"'

We were amused by her story, but that was not the end. Madeleine Carroll went on to tell us that she was recounting these events at a dinner party where she was seated opposite Marlene Dietrich. As she approached the punch line, Marlene Dietrich interrupted, 'Let me guess, "Here's my 75 cents, where's yours," right?'

'I was dumbfounded,' Madeleine Carroll continued. 'Marlene explained that Hughes had done the same to her a few weeks earlier and he was apparently working his way through the whole Hollywood constellation, using identical tactics.'

The venerable star informed us that her house, tucked away in the mountains, was her bolt-hole. Whenever life became too complicated, she would run and she recommended us to adopt the same philosophy. So, shortly afterwards, David established himself in his own bolt-hole in the Port. It was a great place; the boats at anchor beneath his window, restaurants and shops open till midnight or later and people forever walking along the quay – a tiny town that never slept. David said that it was like living in a theatre and I think that many of the adventures or misadventures which befell him arose naturally in that make-believe place.

I loved visiting David in his new apartment, but I was looking for something rather different for myself. We had decided that although we would always stay in contact with each other, we both needed to maintain our independence, so there was no question of sharing a home. I was fortunate in that almost immediately, I came across a large apartment in Marbella itself which suited me perfectly. It was not as pretty as David's, but it was convenient and agreeable and not far from the sea. Being close to the centre of Marbella, there was a wider range of shops and I came into contact with a different set of people from those in the Port, many of whom became my friends.

But the time was approaching when I would have to return to Amsterdam and I was quite proud of the transformation which I had worked on my companion. The night before I left, we went to the Play Bach Bar, just below David's new home. The bar boasted a broken-down, out-of-tune piano and a sequence of pretty bar-maids. I persuaded David to play the wrecked instrument, although it must have been torture for him. I beamed down at my restyled man, fresh from his first visit to a unisex hairdresser.

'You know,' I told him, 'you really are three men in one. For me, you are my Brothers Stein.'

David looked puzzled.

'Well, with your distinguished mop of hair and brilliant, intellectual conversation, you are my Einstein.'

David was flattered and played a few wrong notes in his embarrassment. I watched his fingers, long and sensitive, as they moved over the keys.

'And with your love of music, you are my Rubinstein.'

I regarded him critically and shook my head.

'No, really you are my Frankenstein.'

The resulting cadenza concluded the piano recital. The next day, before I left, I gave David my instructions. He was to keep himself in good shape, write often and while awaiting my return, get about and meet a few girls.

'If I have any problems, I certainly know where to come for advice,' David replied.

I was to learn how fully David had absorbed what he had been taught.

3

Somebody Must Have Four

Back in Amsterdam, I wondered how David was getting along. We had kept in touch by phone, but I wanted a detailed account of his exploits and for that, he assured me, I would have to wait for the arrival of a long letter which he had sent. The bulky envelope flopped on to the doormat one afternoon when I was sitting with Betty, a girlfriend of mine.

I had known Betty for many years but although she was a lesbian, we had only become lovers a few months previously. She was small with a boyish figure, good, firm breasts, and a passionate temperament. Yet she was also an intelligent, coolly logical woman who would criticize me when she considered my conduct to be capricious. A leading member of the women's movement, an outstanding painter, she was one of the few people with whom I had enjoyed a deep relationship which went far beyond mere sex. I had told her about David and I thought that if they were to meet, they would probably become firm friends, for they had a lot in common. I opened David's letter and read it aloud to her.

My Darling Xaviera,

I miss you and Spain is a duller place without you. It is the country of *mañana*, and Alfonso, the guy who runs the gift shop below my apartment, is an expert in missing out and he is teaching me. He also has a vivid imagination. Let me tell you what happened the other day.

There was this girl. She was beautiful, a tall blonde with soft, dreamy eyes, lips full of promise and a lissom figure which had me boggling. Of course, I had not actually seen her, but that was how Alfonso, the Don Juan of the coast, described her. Now, we were on our way to meet this paragon of womanhood who, Alfonso assured me, was as generous with her favours as she was lovely.

To say that we were on our way is a slight exaggeration. Alfonso was searching for her telephone number so that he could call her, find out her address and make a date. And when he got her on the phone, it would be a good idea to discover her name: he only referred to her as 'that damned girl'.

Alfonso is tall and rakish and his full-time occupation is the pursuit (but unfortunately not the attainment) of sexual satisfaction. Since you left, I have been lonely and Alfonso has been an inspiration: without his company I would probably go insane here in six months, but with his assistance, I expect to cut the time by half.

We were in the shop where Alfonso hides his compromising address book from the sharp eyes of Anna, his wife. It was so well hidden that now he could not find it. He tried under the plastic toreador, behind the unsaleable stationery and inside the more gruesome specimens of local pottery without success. The vision of the Venus of Iberia was slowly fading. I was considering how to pass the rest of the day without driving myself into a frenzy of frustration, when a strangled cry of triumph issued from a pile of wrapping paper, and Alfonso emerged, clutching the precious book.

'You see,' he exclaimed, 'I know exactly where to lay my hands on everything. Now, man, just you watch.'

I wondered how he was going to find the number of somebody whose name he could not recall. No problem: he read the book through from cover to cover. By the time he got to Zutphen, it was clear that 'that damned girl' remained as elusive as ever. Alfonso was depressed: no man alive almost knows as many girls as he does. Then he remembered.

'Of course, I did not write it down on some piece of paper where Anna might see it. She gets so jealous. No, I scratched it on the counter in the shop.'

I would not have believed so preposterous a statement from

27

any normal individual: from Alfonso I accepted it without hesitation. What surprised me was that, having solved the mystery, he did not go to read the number. When I asked, he explained that the present counter was new; the inscription we sought was on the old one. I lost my temper.

'So we are simply wasting our time. You've lost the number.'

Alfonso was hurt. All we had to do was to go and look at the old counter, he informed me reproachfully. I visualized touring Spain and scouring all the building sites in the hope of coming across Alfonso's old counter with its magic number, but he put my mind at rest.

'I didn't throw it away. I used it to make the kitchen table at home.'

'So this number which you wanted to hide from Anna is under her nose all day long?'

Alfonso did not deign to answer but he sent me to his flat on some pretext to find the number. If he had put in an appearance, Anna's natural suspicions would have been aroused. I found the table easily enough – no number! Back in the shop I broke the bad news to Alfonso. He was unruffled. When he had cut down the old counter, he must have thrown away the piece of wood on which the number hd been scratched. He obviously could not have cared less if 'that damned girl' had entered a nunnery. There could only be one explanation for his indifference.

'Man, while you were fooling about in my kitchen, the most beautiful girl I have ever seen walked into my shop.'

'Well, where is she?' I challenged.

'She had to go back to change but she is meeting us tonight.'

'Was she as pretty as the other one?' I asked spitefully.

'What other one?' replied the constant lover.

I should have known better, but I turned up that evening to accompany our local Romeo. He runs an ancient Alfa Romeo, named in his honour, I presume, and, like its owner, a bit battered but still sporty. On the road, we passed what appeared to me to be two rather untidy bundles moving in the opposite direction. Without a moment's hesitation, Alfonso did a death-defying U-turn and offered to give the pedestrians a lift. They accepted and climbed in while he chortled in excitement.

'But, Alfonso,' I protested, 'what about this girl who is waiting for us?'

'Exactly,' he agreed. 'She'll wait.'

Of course, she didn't. At least, she was not there when we arrived a couple of hours late. Alfonso was bitterly disappointed at her letting him down. And as for the pair of horrors we had picked up, once they had got to their hotel they explained that they were staying with their parents, thanked us for the lift and wished us a good night.

As we drove home in silence, reflecting on what we had not achieved, Alfonso began to brighten up. He told me that what with the tourists who got sexy because of the sun and the fantastic supply of local girls, Spain was a man's paradise.

'There are two women for every man,' he gloated.

I thought about my solitary bed in my empty flat.

'In that case,' I informed him, 'somebody must have four.'

So, Xaviera, things are pretty quiet and I am trying to keep out of Alfonso's way for a while, but I have a feeling that you have not heard the last of him. When are you coming back to give me another lesson?

Your affectionate pupil, David

Betty was amused by the letter. 'This man needs help,' she commented. 'You ought to go back to Spain and see him.'

I considered. It was tempting. I wanted to buy more furniture for my new apartment and there was the sun and the sea. Also, I was looking forward to checking on how my protégé was shaping up. After all, how seriously should I take his preposterous yarns? He was always making up stories.

'Why don't you come with me?' I asked. 'It would be a holiday for you and more fun for me.'

Betty did not need much persuading and she was intrigued by the prospect of meeting the man who wrote such letters. I called David and told him that a relief expedition would soon be with him. He promised to

29

prepare my apartment and assured me that a great welcome would be waiting for us.

A few days later, we were on the road.

4

The Portuguese Beach Bum

At last I had met a tall, dark and handsome Spanish man. Better, there were two of them. Betty and I were in the car, on the road from Madrid. The sun was beating down and we were tired. I was driving fast and there was heavy traffic. I had just overtaken a crawling truck when I saw this good-looking Spaniard. He beckoned me to stop: he was not trying to hitch a lift, since he and his companion were already on motorbikes. I waved and pulled into the side of the road. The two traffic cops drove up; one got out his notebook, took the number of the car and examined my passport. Unsmilingly, he told me that I was supposed to keep to my own side of the road and not cross the white line. It appeared that I was being given the option of paying a fine or rotting in a Spanish jail.

'Five thousand pesetas!' I screamed. 'That's a hell of a lot!'

The policemen looked at each other.

'Pay now and it's four thousand,' one of them offered.

Betty reached for her purse and paid off the brace of Adonises. They rode away without another glance to find some other hapless female.

'See,' I smiled to Betty, 'I've just saved you a thousand pesetas.'

It was late when we arrived at Marbella, and we decided to have a quiet night at home and put off seeing David until the next day. Maybe the brush with the police had aroused us or perhaps it was that relaxed feeling which comes over me when I get back into a sunny climate, but

I had only one thought in my mind and, as I soon realized, so did Betty.

We climbed into bed and turned off the lights. The moon, shining through the curtainless window, was the only witness to our love-making. Betty's small hands caressed my face and her smooth body rubbed gently against mine. I felt the touch of her full lips on my neck; then she moved my long hair out of the way and started to nibble my earlobe. Although the night was hot, this instantly brought goose-bumps up all over my body. I held her hips and slowly manoeuvred myself until I lay between her legs, her thighs around my face. She smelt marvellous and tasted delicious.

Betty is one of the few women with whom I have made love who, having had a magnificent clitoral orgasm, wants to be finger-fucked immediately afterwards. She begged me to insert my hand in her pulsating pussy while I could still feel her clitoris throbbing against my mouth. Once inside, I closed my fist and I could get nearly the whole of my hand inside her; she was extremely tight yet flexible. It was a fantastic sensation as her vaginal muscles grabbed my hand while her orgasm continued. How I wished then that I had a cock so that I could fuck her properly instead of merely imitating the rhythm of a man. But Betty's response was such that I knew that she was perfectly happy with what I was doing to her. At last, we were sated and we lay still, getting our breath back. Utterly exhausted, but glowing and content, our bodies bathed in sweat, we fell asleep in each other's arms.

In the morning, we went down to the beach where David joined us. Marbella beach is lined with tiny, straw-roofed kitchens and terraces with tables where one can eat simple meals. My favourite was known as Frank's Beach. It was very close to my apartment and had a rather more extensive menu than many of the other *chiringuitos*. Most of the people who went there were English or Swedish: they were young and sociable so it was always easy to get into conversation with somebody.

As I had hoped, David and Betty took to each other at once and were soon discussing art and literature, music and politics. I found that I was participating less and less in their discussion, not because they intended to exclude me, but because I could not get turned on by English antique glass or Dutch Post-Impressionist paintings. My head was simply not into heavy subjects and I was restless.

The trouble was the nature of my relationship with Betty. She was very much in love with me, as I was with her, but she was almost exclusively lesbian and I felt more and more gay when I was with her, despite my reputation as the Great Man-Lover. It seemed to me that no man had ever been able to caress, kiss, suck, or generally make love with the tenderness of that woman, and I began to get the urge to pick up any man or boy to prove to myself that I had not become a total lesbian.

So, as the days went by, I would take to wandering off on any pretext, leaving David and Betty talking together. The beach was hot, sandy and sticky and all I wanted was to get brown and get laid. Of course, they knew what was going on and I was aware that my behaviour really hurt Betty, but I went on slipping back home with kids for whom I did not give a damn. I was just suffering from a horny cunt and the need to show that I was not gay. On one occasion, Betty came home early, and I heard her footsteps in the hallway just as I was approaching my climax. The fear of being caught added to my excitement and I came at the moment that she put her key in the lock. However, usually these casual fucks on the sly did not give me the satisfaction which I was seeking.

33

Betty, who was half Indonesian, had warned me that if she found me cheating and believed that I was trying to hurt her, she might react in one of two very different ways. If she did not simply cry her eyes out, she would become mad and violent. This so-called 'mata-glap' was a national trait: a sudden burst of strength which could easily kill me. Far from deterring me, that danger was a great turn-on.

I was with an English boy called Kevin one day when Betty did catch me. Kevin fled and Betty sat beside me on the sofa. Her eyes had a strange red gleam, and her whole body began to tremble uncontrollably. I held my breath and waited. Then she burst into tears and begged me not to go on picking up beach boys. If I had to find a man, couldn't I be a little bit more discriminating. She assured me that both David and she loved me and that my conduct was hurting both of them. I was moved by her sincerity and for a time confined myself to flirting with my eyes.

I was behaving myself, more or less, but I could not help noticing, during our excursions to Frank's Beach, a handsome young man, probably in his twenties, with a moustache, pitch-black eyes, brown hair and a good, suntanned body. He was always there, but he sat alone and seemed not to know anybody. Someone told me that he was Portuguese and had arrived about a week previously, but apart from that, he remained a mystery man. I speculated wildly about him; who was he and what secrets lay behind those haunting eyes? But I kept my promise to Betty and never approached him.

Then one evening we drove to Fuengirola, about half an hour's ride from Marbella, to go to a discotheque, and who should be there but my Portuguese. Betty had not even seen him, but I decided that Fate must have brought us together. I danced closer and closer to him and let my bare shoulder brush against him or wiggled my ass against his gorgeous buttocks. Soon, we got to talking. My Spanish was good enough for me to follow his mixture of Spanish and Portuguese. After all, we were not exactly strangers; we shared the same beach. He was an excellent dancer and I was getting more and more excited. I had been faithful to Betty for a whole week and while I was happy and having regular orgasms, it still was not the same thing as having a nice, hard cock inside me and resting my head on those hairy shoulders. It was too tempting for me to resist.

I found out that his name was Miguel, he lived in Lisbon and he was a fisherman. I should have thought it odd that a fisherman, who spent his days sitting on the beach, without even buying himself a meal or a drink, should turn up in a fashionable and expensive disco, but, as far as I was concerned, all that mattered was that I was in the arms of a sexy, handsome, charming man and I just wanted to become entangled and to melt into his body as soon as possible.

So, at half-past two, the three of us were in my car, on the way back to my place. Betty had a sad expression in her eyes and she made it clear that she did not approve of my conquest, but I was too horny to care. I suggested to Miguel that he spend the night with me and the next morning we would all go to another beach, Santa Marta. Meanwhile, perhaps he would like to call in at his hotel to pick up a few of his things. He was strangely reluctant to tell me where he was staying, but finally asked me to pass by the Don Miguel. I knew this hotel by name, and I had heard that it was a lovely place, but I had never been there, so I asked my Miguel to show me the way.

His directions were vague and confusing and we got completely lost.

'How long have you been staying at this hotel?' I asked him.

'About a week.'

'So how is it that you don't know where it is?'

He muttered something about always taking taxis and then said that he was wearing his bathing trunks beneath his clothes and there was nothing that he needed urgently for the next day, so we could skip going to his hotel. I thought that his story was a bit bizarre. Was it a coincidence that he was staying at a hotel with the same name as his own? But it was a relief to be able to head back to my apartment instead of wandering along the winding country roads in the dark, and I dismissed my suspicions.

When we got home, Betty retired to the guest bedroom which was separated from my room by a bathroom. She had some work to do and was accustomed to keeping late hours, so when I slipped in to say goodnight, she was under the sheet, naked, with a writing pad propped up on her lap and her glasses perched on her nose. She looked so cute that I could have made love to her on the spot.

However, Miguel was in the bathroom, freshening up, and when I put my head round the door, he whispered, 'What's going on with Betty? Is she joining us?'

'No, Betty does not like men,' I informed him. 'Tonight, you and I will make love in my room and she will not interfere. But she can be quite jealous, so mind that you leave her alone.'

Miguel had wrapped a thick, white towel around his splendid, scented body, but instead of following me, turned the other way and barged into Betty's room. She was startled by this invasion of her privacy: her glasses fell on to the sheet and I could see that she was in no mood to be pestered by some man. But Miguel was not discouraged. A stiff cock does not do much thinking, and his erection was enormous. He tried to pull me into the bed also, which annoyed me as much as it did Betty. She was on the point of clawing his eyes out and I had lost all interest in him but his reaction seemed pretty normal for an over-sexed man, so I dragged him off to my room to fuck him and get rid of his hard-on as quickly as possible so that we could get to sleep. I was thoroughly turned off, but Miguel concluded that if his threesome was not going to work out, he had better settle for what was on offer. We fucked, or more accurately, I got fucked fast and furiously. He pumped away so violently that I hit my head on the wall repeatedly: Betty must have wondered whether this was an SOS call. We rolled all over the bed, but after about fifteen strokes, he came with a shriek like a wounded animal. I faked an orgasm for his benefit but, although he had a beautiful body and a good cock, I could not bear to have him in me a moment longer. I threw him out of the bed and did not bother to hand him a towel or even a tissue.

'Get into that other bedroom,' I ordered him. 'Betty is coming in here: I want to sleep with my true lover.'

His sperm was leaking all over my sheet but I could not give a damn. All I wanted was to see the back of him. Betty looked annoyed when we pushed our way into her room again, but was content enough when she understood that I had come to fetch her to spend the rest of the night with me. However, she insisted that I wash myself meticulously and gargle before she would come to bed with me. We made love sweetly and tenderly and gradually the tension eased. We were talking quietly before going to sleep when I heard Miguel shuffling about in the living

37

room. I shouted to him and he called that he was looking for his cigarettes.

'That's strange,' I told Betty. 'It's four o'clock and he wants his cigarettes. They were here beside my bed and he took them with him into the other room.'

'I don't trust the bastard,' she replied, 'he's probably prowling around, looking for any money or valuables that have been left where he can lay his hands on them.'

'Oh, my God! I've left my purse on the table. It's got thousands of pesetas in it.'

'Calm down,' Betty smiled. 'I never liked the look of him. I locked your purse in the wardrobe and I have the key.'

I sighed with relief that I had somebody like Betty to look after me. The flat was still once more, and we settled down to sleep.

In the morning, I went into the guest bedroom and woke up Miguel who was snoring, comfortably stretched out in the king-sized bed. With a yawn, he stepped into the clumsy clogs which he had worn ever since I first saw him, even in the disco where he had trodden on my toes, but when he was sneaking furtively around the apartment in the early hours of the morning he was barefoot. The sound of those clogs was something which I was going to remember for a long time. I got busy fixing breakfast and Miguel revealed that he possessed a prodigious appetite. No matter what he was offered, he accepted readily: yoghurt, watermelon, eggs, ham, cheese, anything that was available, and while I worked, he sat back and watched. He was too idle to walk into the next room for his cigarettes, but asked me to fetch them for him. The meal over, I had some shopping to do and he wanted to borrow my motorbike. I did not think it too clever an idea to let him ride off with it, so I only allowed him to take it into town with me sitting on the pillion.

At last, the three of us were lying in the sun on the Santa Marta beach. I paid for three beach mattresses; so far my gallant escort had not put his hand in his pocket once in my presence, and he retained this record for the rest of the time that we were together. Not that he was poor, at least according to the stories he told me about his wealthy family. But a few minutes later, he was describing the poverty of his parents, living in a tiny fishing village, and how he had been sent to sea without even having been able to go to school. By the time that Vic, an old Dutch friend of mine, arrived, I had grown tired of Miguel's compulsive lying and I chatted to Vic in Dutch. Miguel strolled off and returned with a Coke which he had begged, borrowed, stolen or, just conceivably, bought. His selfishness infuriated me.

'Thanks for offering me a drink,' I remarked sarcastically.

'I don't have any more money on me,' he retorted.

'I thought that you had a few hundred pesetas when we were in town.'

'I bought cigarettes. Now I have no change.'

I grabbed the half-empty bottle from him and finished the Coke.

'It was kind of you to share your drink with me,' I told him.

He glared at me, but said nothing. His sullenness irritated Betty and Vic as well as myself, and when Vic later invited Betty and me for lunch, Miguel was pointedly excluded. Nevertheless, when we were seated at the table, there was that unmistakable clatter of his clogs, and he pulled up a chair and joined us. The three of us ordered simple beach fare, salads and chicken: Miguel called for scampi, by far the most expensive item on the menu, and a double portion! He ignored us and, having devoured the contents of one plate, shouted repeatedly for his second helping. That was too much. I turned to Armand, the Belgian manager of Santa Marta, a gentle, courteous man and a good friend of mine, and said, 'Armand, cancel that second portion. I apologize for bringing this rude bastard to your place.'

As it happened, our uninvited guest must have had sufficient to eat, since he almost immediately fell asleep. I awoke him in the middle of the afternoon, as I had to get back to the apartment for the delivery of an armchair which I had bought. We started to walk back up the path to where the car was parked, and I asked Miguel to carry my beach bag. He pointed to Vic.

'Let him carry it. I am too tired.'

When I had finished telling him what I thought of his manners and his behaviour in general, he picked up the bag and slunk back to the car with it. As for me, I could not get home quickly enough so as to be able to drop him off. When we arrived, I turned to him and said, '*Muchas gracias*, Miguel, and *adios*. I never want to see you again.'

When I opened the front door, he followed Betty and Vic inside and explained that he had left some money in the bedroom.

'I thought that you said on the beach that you did not have any money,' I snapped.

'I have some, and some traveller's cheques. They are here somewhere.'

'Hurry up and find them: then get out,' I ordered.

He looked around but found nothing and when I eventually threw him out, he had the cheek to accuse me of stealing his money. It was the next day that I found the battered, shabby wallet, tucked into a corner of my wardrobe.

'Did you put this here?' I asked Betty.

'Yes, when I tidied up the room before we went to Santa Marta. I thought that it was one of yours which you had left on the table after breakfast.'

'It's not mine. I suppose it must belong to that jerk, Miguel. We might as well see what's inside.'

The contents came as a surprise. In addition to a few British pounds, there were six cheques, drawn on a Geneva bank, and totalling about half a million Swiss francs. They were signed by a Peggy Meyer, but five of the signatures looked as if they were rather amateurish copies of the other one. Quite a bit of money for an impoverished Portuguese fisherman who could not afford to buy me a bottle of Coke! I guessed that the cheques were stolen, but was not sure what to do with them. As for the cash, I decided that I had a right to take that as compensation for the lousy time Miguel had given us, and Betty and I bought a few pieces of inexpensive jewellery in the Old Town, by way of celebration.

When David came round, I told him what had happened, showed him the cheques and asked him for his advice.

He was emphatic. 'Tear them up and flush them down the toilet! If you take them to the police or send them to the bank, you could have a tough time explaining how they came to be in your possession. They are obviously forged and they must have been stolen from the unfortunate Madam Meyer, whoever she may be.'

About four days later, Betty and I had come back from the beach and were taking a bath together to rinse off the sand, salt and sweat. We had a dinner date with David, but intended to have a leisurely session of love-making and a snooze before he arrived. I was pouring shampoo on my hair, when I was disturbed by a loud and repeated ringing of the doorbell. I wrapped a towel around me, and with the shampoo still in my hair, ran to the door, leaving a trail of puddles. There, in uniform, stood a member of the Guardia Civil and a man who turned out to be a plain-clothes policeman. I sensed immediately that their business concerned Miguel. They asked me about the wallet and informed me that I had been accused of stealing it and its contents. I reacted indignantly and part of what I told them was true.

'Sure, I found a worn-out old wallet here after a man who had tried to rob us had left the apartment. It was empty.'

'Our information is that there were personal cheques and a lot of foreign money in it.'

I threw the wallet on the table. 'That's how I found it, empty. How dare that creep accuse me! He was with us in a supermarket during the day; I expect that, if he ever had that money, he dropped it there.'

The policeman insisted that the two of us go with him in spite of all my protests that we had nothing whatever to do with their investigation. So we dried ourselves, pulled on some clothes and were marched off to the waiting police car.

During the journey, the plain-clothes man unbent and told us what had happened. Miguel was being held at Torremolinos, where he had been caught attempting to commit a robbery. I realized then why we had picked him up at Fuengirola, which is between Torremolinos and Marbella. He must have stolen the cheques and money from Peggy Meyer and then left Marbella to let things cool off. We had brought him back and he had tried feebly to rob me, but in the process had lost what he had

42

previously stolen through his own stupidity. Then, he had hitch-hiked to Torremolinos, where he was arrested as a 'balcony thief'. Now, he was being brought back to Marbella to confront us, and Betty and I were obliged to wait for him in the bleak, stuffy police station. Once there, the police talked freely. I gathered that we were required to identify him and that he looked set fair to enjoy three years of Spanish hospitality. Meanwhile, our dinner date was clearly off.

'Do we really have to wait here?' I complained. 'It's hot, I am uncomfortable and I want to go home.'

'It's more uncomfortable on the other side of the bars,' the officer in charge informed me.

Finally, I heard the familiar and hated clopping of those clogs. I could hardly recognize Miguel. He had been pretty badly beaten up. His hair was greasy and hung over his bruised eye. There were scratches all over his face and he was filthy and badly needed a shave.

'Why did you bring up my name?' I hissed at him. I knew that the policeman who was with us spoke no English.

'You stole my wallet,' he replied.

'Now listen, you lying bastard. You go along with my account that you must have dropped your wallet in the supermarket. Otherwise, I'll give them the cheques you stole and you will be an old man before they let you out of jail.'

Of course, he did not know that I had already destroyed the evidence, so he attempted to do a deal with me and get me to find him a lawyer – and pay the bill.

'Pay for a lawyer for you after you tried to rob me too!' I shouted. 'And Christ knows how many other women you have ripped off. Now, what are you going to tell the police?'

Reluctantly, he agreed to change his story: he must have dropped his money and cheques when he was in the supermarket or in the street outside. So ended the story of the Portuguese beach bum, or so we thought.

A few days later, David called on us. He had a knowing smile on his lips.

'It's a small world,' he observed. 'Do you remember that pretty boutique close to my apartment, Elle et Lui? I was in there yesterday, talking to the woman who owns it. She told me how upset she was as she had just been robbed by some guy who had broken into her flat from the balcony and stolen, among other things, a batch of her cheques, including one which she had foolishly signed and left blank. She is Swiss and was dreadfully worried that the cheques would be forged and cashed before she could warn the bank in Geneva.'

'Her name would not be Peggy Meyer, by any chance?' I enquired.

David nodded. 'And was she relieved when I told her that her cheques had gone down your toilet!'

'I think I'll get a stronger lock fitted to the doors of my balcony,' I said with a smile. 'Now, how about that dinner you owe us?'

5

The Stripper and the Queen

David had taken Betty and me to a party where we met a lot of strange people, but nobody was stranger than Bobby. We had been waiting for a meal which had been promised but was taking its time to appear, and I found myself talking with a strong-featured, German lesbian named Bettina. The way she eyed my breasts suggested that, in her opinion, the food could come later. She was wearing close-fitting, black trousers and long boots made of supple leather. I watched her keen, intelligent face as she told me that she was an interior decorator. I mentioned the name of the man who had worked for me in my apartment.

Bettina laughed scornfully. 'Him? He'll discuss interminably with some poor client the design for a place and a colour scheme. Once you have decided that you want your place painted green, he'll turn up next day with a can of red paint. I certainly would not want him decorating my interior.'

From my experience, I felt that Bettina had a point, but I cut short our conversation. On the other side of the room, I had spotted David talking to an exotic-looking young man. He looked unhappy: his eyes caught mine and flashed a mute but urgent appeal for help. I excused myself and crossed the room to render what assistance I could. David introduced me to Bobby with a sigh of relief. Bobby was of medium height and not at all unusual in appearance, apart from the fact that he wore rather charming little earrings, a full-length, slit scarlet kaftan and false eyelashes. With his long golden hair and liquid blue eyes, Bobby flaunted his gayness, shooting provocative smiles at David and squeezing his hand. David was obviously uncomfortable, so I reminded him of our non-existent date at the other end of town. We picked up Betty, made our farewells and departed.

'What's the matter?' I asked David. 'Don't you find your very feminine friend attractive?'

'Bloody Bobby,' he moaned. 'He chases me everywhere. I wish that the earth would open and swallow up that Cleopatra with a cock.'

I would not have believed that within a matter of days David would be eagerly welcoming Bobby's company, but that was before he told me about Claudine.

Betty and I were away for several days, visiting friends, and it was a couple of weeks later that we met David again in one of the intimate bars in the Old Town. He was in a good humour and listened attentively to our news. Mischievously, I asked him how his affair with Bobby was progressing.

'Bobby!' David chuckled. 'He has gone, vanished, evaporated and I am free. Mind you, the last month or so has been a reasonable preview of hell, what with Bobby, Alfonso and Claudine.'

'Claudine? That's a new one. What have you been up to?'

'That's a long story.'

'We have the whole evening before us,' I grinned. 'I am curious to hear the latest exploits of Alfonso and how your love life is blossoming. What do you say, Betty?'

'Come on, David,' Betty urged. 'I can see that you are aching to tell us one of your epic adventures.'

David ordered a round of drinks and settled down to his narrative. 'Have you ever thought how easily the

46

hunter can become the hunted?' he began. 'All through the summer, I have been invited by Alfonso to join him in his non-existent orgies. Unchastened by each rebuff, the gallant caballero sits in his shop, planning ever more daring onslaughts on embattled womankind. For my part, neither his customers nor local tradesmen tend to take much notice of me, but there was one exception. I mentioned to Alfonso that a Spanish girl who frequented the restaurant next door seemed to be paying me a great deal of attention. "That's Claudine," Alfonso explained breezily. "She saw your Rolls Royce outside my shop and wanted to know who owned it and how much it cost. I said fifty million pesetas – it sounded a good, round sum and she seemed impressed. She asked if you were married and whether you preferred blondes or brunettes. I told her that you were interested in anything that was going, and she said that she was pleased since that would save her the trouble of having her hair dyed." I felt that he was a bit unfair, but there is no point in arguing with Alfonso, so I asked him why, for someone who was obsessed by chasing girls, he was so indifferent to Claudine. She was not at all bad-looking.

'"She is a stripper at The Golden Slipper," he told me disdainfully. "I can introduce you, if that is what you would like." Judging by the way she was ogling me, I was sure that an introduction would be superfluous, but I could still not fathom Alfonso's coolness. "I have never known you exclude a woman from your shopping list on the grounds of her occupation," I observed. "I'm not at all sure that it would not be a breach of some human rights legislation and you could find yourself up before the International Court of Justice." Alfonso muttered something about fixing myself up with a good doctor if I intended dating Claudine, since she went with everybody.

"Then why is she always sitting alone when she is here?" I demanded. "Giovanni considers her to be his girlfriend and he is very jealous," Alfonso explained, and he nodded in the direction of the Sicilian waiter at the restaurant.

'That was when I became aware of a hate-filled scowl, hovering about six feet from the floor, and aimed directly at me. Around the scowl was the most malevolent face I had seen for quite a while. As if to confirm his worst suspicions, Claudine flashed a dazzling smile at me and nodded suggestively towards the door. Alfonso, meanwhile, retailed the list of Giovanni's brothers, cousins and other bloodthirsty Sicilians, all of whom were ready to avenge any slight to his honour, real or imaginary. I began to understand why Alfonso was so impervious to the charms of Claudine, which were so lavishly and ostentatiously displayed. I glanced again at the hostile waiter, and lust died in my loins.

'After that, my life was turned into a monstrous game of hide-and-seek. I hid, Claudine sought and Giovanni played umpire. I suffered a setback when Claudine discovered the entrance to my apartment and began lurking outside, so I started to invite friends to come upstairs with me and escort me through the danger zone.'

'That's all very well,' Betty interrupted, 'but what has it to do with Bobby?'

'I was coming to that,' David replied. He clearly resented having us break into the flow of his narrative. 'Coming back from the beach one day with a group of loungers and scroungers, I found Bobby standing outside Alfonso's shop, inspecting the Rolls Royce. "Is that your car: how much did it cost?" he asked. I felt that I had been here before. "No," I said, "it belongs to an acquaintance who is an undertaker and during the week it is used as a hearse." Bobby giggled. "Cheeky!" he lisped.

48

'Looking around, I was not encouraged by the presence of Claudine, whose lurking had become even more purposeful, and Giovanni, on the terrace of the restaurant, pensively fingering some knives. I proposed to my companions that they come up for a drink, but they all refused and, to my consternation, my protective shield of henchmen and women melted away. Claudine was obviously delighted: Giovanni stiffened and concentrated more intensely on his knives. I was aroused from my panic by the voice of Bobby. "Ta ever so, just a teeny one." His eyes were darting little messages to me as urgently as those of Claudine, and I hesitated. Then I read the message in Giovanni's eyes and I hesitated no longer. Once upstairs, Bobby made himself comfortable and my next problem was how to get rid of him before he took root. "Drink up, er, laddy," I prompted, "I have to drive to the airport to pick up my girlfriend who is flying in from Paris." Bobby looked puzzled and pointed out that there was no flight due from France. "A slip of the tongue," I assured him, "I meant London. And she has probably changed at Barcelona or somewhere. Anyway, I must be on my way: out you go!" He could not understand how I might prefer the company of a woman to his, but allowed himself to be hustled out. At the doorway, he paused and warned me that he had noticed Claudine hanging about. "She is a poisonous bitch; steer well clear of her. See you soon, say tomorrow?" and he minced off.

'Sure enough, next day Bobby was very much in evidence. He was busy making a golden bikini for a girl, or so he said, but I had my doubts, which were increased when he gave me an account of a beauty contest which had recently been held in Ibiza. It seemed that Bobby, in full drag, had entered and had wiped the floor with the competition. "You have no idea of the fuss when I revealed myself," he purred. "They wanted to disqualify me, but I said, what about sex equality? I thought that I had them cornered, but they claimed that I had cheated by wearing a wig. They got nasty, so I whipped off my bikini and showed them what I had. Next day I was asked, politely but firmly, to leave the island, so here I am, darling, back looking for nice friends, like you." I felt that the time had come for us to part, and I informed him that I was going to lunch. "Thanks," he said, and trotted off by my side. "I'm expecting friends," I lied. "That's all right, I don't mind; there will be plenty of room." And from then on, he became my inseparable companion.

'There was a consolation for me in the marked slackening of interest by Claudine, but I was not prepared for Alfonso's suddenly asking if I had gone queer. "It's simply that Bobby is telling everybody that you are crazy about him," he explained. "You are forever buying him meals and drinks. He says that he is moving in with you, and the two of you are off tomorrow to choose a new bed." I informed Alfonso that Bobby was a vicious little turd and that Alfonso ought to know me well enough to see through his fantasies. Alfonso looked doubtful and remarked that he had noticed how my passion for Claudine had withered. "After your glowing account of her as a syphilitic mafia godmother, only a man with an overwhelming desire to commit suicide in the messiest manner possible would give her a second glance," I remonstrated. Alfonso replied that he did not know that I was so easily put off. "Still, if you prefer fairies," he sneered, and he strode off, dismissing me with a contemptuous nod.

'As far as I was concerned, Bobby had now become Public Enemy No. 1, and I began a policy of avoiding him. When he called, I was always on my way out, and I changed my usual watering holes. Finally, the message got through and I was once more left in peace.

'Then, late one night, there was a knock on my door. I opened it and was astonished to find Bobby standing there. But it was a very different Bobby from the old, carefree, arrogant exhibitionist. He was tense and distraught and apologized for disturbing me. He told me that, having run short of cash, he had left a valuable diamond ring with a friendly boutique owner to try to sell. The shop was a trendy place and very popular with the sort of people who might buy a piece of good jewellery. It appeared that his arch-enemy, Claudine, had looked at the ring, deterred a potential buyer by suggesting that the stone was a fake, and hatched out a plot with Emilia, the girl who worked at the boutique. That morning, the ring was missing from its box, and Emilia was flying to Madrid by the night plane. Bobby was sure that the two girls had conspired to steal his ring and he begged me to lend him a couple of thousand pesetas so that he could take a taxi to the airport and catch Emilia before she could get away. I willingly complied. Although I did not expect Bobby to repay the debt, I considered that this would be a cheap price to pay for being totally free of his embarrassing company. He thanked me effusively and hurried away.

'But I had misjudged him. Next day, he was back and pressed two thousand-peseta notes into my hand. I was startled: it was like being given a second chance by a black mamba. When I asked him if he had been able to intercept Emilia and recover his ring, he told me he had stopped her, and a couple of policemen had gone over her luggage. "The ring wasn't there and the silly bitch burst into tears. She must have hidden it, or given it to Claudine," he remarked, with unexpected calm. I found his behaviour strange, but it was not my business and I dismissed the matter.

'Yesterday, I was talking with Alfonso; I mentioned that I had not seen Bobby around for several days and wondered if he had ever got his ring back. Alfonso laughed. "There never was a ring and Bobby has flown to London. He did ask me if I would change a cheque for ten thousand pesetas for him, but I told him that I did not have any money in the shop. However, he got about half a dozen other shopkeepers to change cheques for his accomplice." I began to see the light. "They bounced?" Alfonso grinned and nodded. "Which of the pretty boys was in the racket with him?" I wanted to know. "What makes you think there was a boy involved?" My neighbour was amused by my naïvety. "He's run off with Claudine: they have been working together for months. I suppose Giovanni will get over the shock one day."

'So, Xaviera, I guess that we have heard the last of Bobby and his diamond ring.'

As it happened, David was mistaken. A few months later I got a phone call from Bobby, who was in London and had found out my number in Spain. He invited me to come over and manage a new brothel which, he claimed, he had recently opened and which was proving to be an outstanding success. He was running a Rolls Royce and had God knows how many girls working for him. He had luxurious premises in the West End, and it had all been achieved within six weeks.

I declined his kind offer. I remembered Bobby's jewellery which flashed in his ears or on his fingers. Somehow, the one ring which was missing was the ring of truth.

6

Interlude: Vienna–Rome

At the end of the summer season in Marbella I decided to go to the Oktoberfest in Munich, and I invited David to accompany me, but when we went to a travel agent, we found that all the better hotels were already full, so we abandoned the idea. However, we thought that we could have fun if we went away together for two or three weeks anyway, and, after considering the alternatives, came down in favour of a short holiday split between Vienna and Rome.

So, in the middle of September, I drove back to Amsterdam, where I was joined a week later by David who flew in from Malaga, and after a few days' shopping, we took the early flight to Vienna. Of course, it had to be that morning that my car, which had performed perfectly right through the round trip to Marbella and back, refused to start. My mother, loyal and reliable as always, on hearing of our plight jumped out of bed and drove over to my house, picked us up and got us to Schiphol in time for our plane. A couple of hours later, still bleary-eyed, we were in the airport in Vienna, waiting for our luggage.

We were standing beside the conveyor belt when we were pushed aside by a large, important-looking Alsatian dog. The animal had the air of one who belonged there and was absolutely self-assured. We were amused when it climbed on to the belt, which had been set in motion, and walked in the opposite direction, so that it appeared to be marking time. It looked like a circus act, but when the baggage began to arrive and the dog sniffed every case,

53

we realized that this was no comic turn. Our companion was a police dog, specially trained to detect drugs.

In the taxi, I chatted to the driver. He was the first man I had met who admitted unashamedly that he had fought in the German army against the British and Americans and was proud of his war record. Both David and myself were sick of meeting people who explained that they were Austrians, not Germans, and so had played no part in the War, or that they had served unwillingly, and had been employed as pastry cooks. It was fantastic, David remarked drily, how close Hitler came to winning the War with an army consisting entirely of pastry cooks. Our taxi driver was the exception. He suffered no qualms of conscience, nor did he bear any hostility towards his former enemies, or so he said, but I suspect that he overcharged us.

We had chosen our hotel for its quiet location, since it stood at the end of the Karntnerstrasse, a fashionable, shop-lined pedestrian street. The absence of motor traffic assured tranquillity, we read in the brochure. One minor circumstance which did disturb the promised calm of the place had not been brought to our notice. The Viennese were constructing a new underground railway system, and a major excavation was in progress directly outside the hotel. In fact, to get into the front door we had to clamber over a pile of planks, and our bedroom window looked out on to this yawning chasm where men were working furiously – and very noisily.

Of course, we did the sightseeing round of the magnificent buildings and monuments of the city and managed to get seats for a performance of a Mozart opera in the Staatsoper. David, who had suffered in Marbella from being deprived of any cultural activity, was all for making up for lost time, and proposed going to a performance of

Tristan und Isolde, but I persuaded him to settle for lighter fare, and we ended up at the Volksoper for a delightfully frothy performance of one of those light-hearted operettas, *Der Vogelhandler* by Karl Zeller. Eventually, I had my fill of tramping round the art galleries, and David visited some on his own, while I took things easier and met a few interesting people.

However, one outing we did do together was to the palace of Schönbrunn. I was greatly impressed by the rococo splendour of the building, standing in its formal gardens on the wooded slopes, which were outside the city when the palace was built. I had passed through the gold and white doors and was fantasizing about elegant aristocrats in satin waistcoats and knee breeches, and imperial ladies in long, flowing gowns with their jewels glittering under the chandeliers, when I was brought back to the present by somebody tapping me on the shoulder and calling out, 'Hello, Xaviera, long time no see.'

The man who stood before me was not decked out in Habsburg court dress, but wore a sports shirt and blue jeans. I recognized Rudi, an Austrian friend from my days in Canada. He had a lean, suntanned face and rather sparse brown hair. Behind his horn-rimmed glasses, his eyes had a pleasant, sprightly expression. Rudi was gay and with him was his boyfriend, Walter. I introduced David, and we were invited to have dinner with them and to meet Walter's mother.

That evening we went to a Hungarian restaurant, well known both for its cuisine and its ambience. We ate well and the conversation was lively. Both the boys were young, intelligent and good-looking, each in his own way, but it was Walter's mother who stole the show. Lily was a youngster of about seventy-five, with soft, grey eyes and a sweet smile, who looked as if she were approaching fifty. I earned her approval when, at the end of the meal, I walked over to the cembalo player and thanked him for his music in more or less fluent Hungarian, which completely exhausted my knowledge of that language. From his reply, I gathered that he would have welcomed the opportunity to extend my vocabulary in a private session, but I had other plans. The time passed so quickly and so enjoyably that I accepted with pleasure Rudi's suggestion that we go to a Heuring with them.

Rudi explained that the Heuring was a sort of wine festival and that all around Vienna we would find inns and taverns with small bushes hanging from their doors. This meant that they were selling wine, made from grapes grown in their own vineyards, which was very cheap since it was exempted from tax. It would be young wine, the vintage of that year. Although the new wine was sold in one place or another for practically the whole year, September and October were the best months for enjoying the celebrations in the cheerful taverns in the picturesque villages of the Wienerwald. There would be plenty of eating, drinking and singing, we were told. A couple of nights later, we were on our way to Grinzing.

During the afternoon David had been somewhat restless, and I suddenly felt a tremendous desire for sexual satisfaction, but not in the usual manner. Our days were so full that I did not have the time I wanted to act out all my fantasies in bed, and I had tantalized David by refusing him any form of sex for several days. He had always treated me with the greatest kindness and consideration so I cannot explain why I should have derived pleasure from inflicting suffering on him. However, before we left the hotel I made him watch me as I masturbated in the bath. I held the shower head so that the water sprayed directly on to my clitoris and when

David took his rigid cock in his hand, I ordered him to stop and would not allow him to shoot his sperm into the bath water. He was pretty agitated by the time I had dressed, and he seemed to be particularly turned on by a sensuous, purple silk scarf which I was wearing to go with the pastel shades of my blouse and skirt. When he tried to approach me I pushed him away, but my game was interrupted by the arrival of Rudi to drive us to Grinzing.

Tucked away between hills in the forest, Grinzing had a fairytale charm. It was favoured by the artistic community, and it managed to be both Bohemian and fashionable. All around us were inns, looking like a stage setting for an operetta, and the village was thronged by great crowds of happy Viennese, eating, singing, dancing and, above all, drinking.

I do not drink, but it was impossible not to be swept along in the joyful, carnival atmosphere. We joined in the Heuring in a monster tavern where six or seven very large rooms were all packed with men and women, sitting on forms before bare, wooden tables. Every available spot had been taken, but Rudi had previously reserved our places. We ate bread and sausages, ham and cheese, and while the wine flowed groups of men in local costume played accordions. Everyone linked arms and swayed drunkenly from side to side, while they sang boisterously their old, favourite songs.

Lily was in her element. She was decorously dressed in a rather low-cut dirndl dress, and Rudi told us with obvious pride that his mother had never worn a brassiere. Her eyes twinkled, and she began to flirt outrageously with David. She patted his hand with all the arch coyness of a teenager: he was quite flattered by her attentions, but not sure how to react.

As the night went on the singing grew louder, the great

jugs of wine circulated more rapidly and the merry-makers became less and less inhibited, but at last the time came for Rudi to take us back to our hotel.

Both David and I were still very wide awake, and I was in the mood to realize my earlier fantasies. I sensed that David too was erotically aroused and ready for the fulfilment which I had sadistically denied him. I undressed slowly and languorously and was standing before him in my bra and panties, when I remembered how he had been attracted by my scarf before we went to Grinzing.

I smiled at him slyly. 'So you like my scarf, do you?'

He nodded, not knowing what to expect.

'Take off your clothes,' I hissed.

He did as he was told, and when he was naked I took my scarf and wound it around his eyes, completely blindfolding him. After the excitement of the Heuring we were ready for some new, sensual adventure.

'Remember the other day, we visited the Spanish Riding School?' I said. 'Well, we are going to have our own private riding school here. We don't need a horse: I shall ride you round the room. You would like that, wouldn't you?'

I did not give him the chance to answer, but roughly pushed him on to his hands and knees and climbed on to his back. 'Now, trot!' I commanded, and slapped his bare rump.

I pressed my thighs into my steed and guided him round the room. Then another idea came to me. 'Have you ever been in bondage?' I asked, 'Really tied up, so that you could not move?'

'No,' David murmured, but there was something in his voice which convinced me that he was intrigued by the prospect of being truly helpless. I grabbed his hands and twisted them behind his back. Then, using his tie and my nylons, I fastened his hands securely and bound his feet at the ankles. He was still blindfolded, lying on the carpet. I walkled over to the bed and told him that he was to crawl to me. The situation was very sexy in a kinky way, but it had its absurd side and both of us were giggling wildly. It took him quite a time to get to the bed, but he made it eventually. However, I had not finished tormenting him yet and I found another of his ties, with which I bound up his cock. He had a gigantic erection and I was worried that I might have tied the knot too tight, since his cock went a delicate and rather attractive shade of purple. I dragged him over to a swivel chair beside the bed and helped him to climb into it. I spun him around until he was so giddy that he could not stand up when I released his bonds. Our game had become hectic, and we knocked over the telephone, an ancient, heavy, Bakelite affair, cracking the case. As it still functioned, we did not give the matter another thought: we had other things on our minds.

Before he could recover his balance, I pulled him on to the bed and literally raped him. David was as meek as a lamb, ready to take whatever I handed out. I mounted him, forcing myself down on to him, at the same time grasping his hands and holding them tightly behind his head. I was soaking wet from my own excitement, and my pussy quivered uncontrollably as I felt his great prick penetrate me and reach right up beyond my navel. It was as though I could draw the whole of him into me and devour him with my raging cunt. I ripped off his blindfold, and David looked up at me like a stricken animal as I sucked him in. I was fucking him hard and passionately: he was unable to stir, for I had him pinned down and absolutely at my mercy. His mouth sagged half open, and his eyes rolled wildly. I knew that I had him in my power:

he would do anything I commanded. He moaned that he was mine, and begged me to do whatever I wanted with him.

'Now fuck me good and hard,' I told him, squeezing his hands yet more savagely. 'Fill me with all that semen you have had to save up for me. I want every drop that you have in those big, beautiful balls of yours. Put it in really deep, as far as it will go.'

He was thrusting up from under my body, and I could tell that he was near to bursting.

'Wait!' I called. 'Not yet.'

He was desperate and pleaded to be allowed to come inside me. He had been deprived for so long that the suspense was driving him crazy. But every time he came close to his climax, I would jump up from his cock. Leaning back on my heels, I knelt above him and grasped his trembling, wet member with my hand, preventing him from ejaculating. Sometimes, when he was on the brink, I would bite it softly or bind it again with one of my nylons.

Then once more I sat down on him, and this time I reversed our roles. It was no longer David who was penetrating me, but I was the proud owner of that magnificent cock, and he was my helpless woman whose cunt I was pounding. I closed my legs tight and pressed down heavily on him: he accepted the switch, and curled his legs around my waist like a compliant female.

'How does that grab you?' I demanded. 'Now you have become my WHORE!'

'It's marvellous. Don't stop, darling, I have never been fucked like this before.'

I pumped harder than ever, and felt his legs gripping me more urgently, as if craving for me to possess him.

'I want you to open your eyes when you come. Look at

me, you whore, see how a real guy fucks a woman.' My voice was harsh and masterful.

As I spoke, I could not hold myself back any longer. I rubbed my clitoris hard against the base of his cock, and with a tremendous surge, we came simultaneously.

There had been nothing subtle about our sex game that night, but its very weirdness had added somehow to our passion. It was as though all the singing and dancing at the Heuring, the excitement of the crowds and the festive atmosphere, had led inevitably to our own special climax to round off a fantastic evening.

Maybe there was something symbolic in our playing out the slavery-bondage fantasy, for had I not had time to order David about for months while I reshaped his life-style. This was a phase of his life from which he was now emerging very much his own man again.

Next morning, there was an unexpected sequel to our exploit. We had been exhausted and slept heavily until we eventually descended to take our breakfast. The manager greeted David with a friendly smile after the meal.

'Excuse me, Sir, but I believe you had a slight accident with your telephone.'

'Oh, yes,' replied David. 'It somehow got knocked over.'

I could not restrain a smile at the tact of his understatement.

'It will be necessary for the phone to be repaired,' the manager said.

'I understand. However, it works all right, so it should not be a big job.'

'Unfortunately, it will be necessary for us to replace the phone and I am obliged to add the cost to your bill.' The manager's expression was sympathetic, but adamant.

'How much?' asked David resignedly.

The manager mentioned some astronomical figure. David seemed unperturbed. 'Fine, just wrap it up securely with string and brown paper, please.'

The manager was puzzled.

David explained: 'You insist that although the phone is not badly damaged, you have to buy a new one and you are charging me a grossly exaggerated price for it. Since I am paying for the new phone, I reckon that the old one is now my property, and I would like to take it with me, as a souvenir of your generosity.'

I did not see our bill when we left the hotel, but I believe that David's irony paid off. However, they did add thirty per cent to the cost of our tickets for the opera which we had ordered at the hotel since, as they told us, they had to send their messenger round to pick them up. So much for the famed Viennese courtesy!

But our minds were already on Rome, for we were on the point of leaving for the second half of our holiday, and I had my own particular reason to look forward to the Eternal City. While I was in Marbella, Daniël had mentioned that he had lived for some time in Rome, and had a lot of friends there. I had asked him to give me a few names of interesting people whom I could look up, since I was certain that David would want to visit more historic sites and cultural masterpieces than I could take, and he had already agreed that I should take some time off on my own to do my own thing. Daniël had given me a list, but sworn me to secrecy. I was not to disclose my names to David, as this could lead to embarrassment for Daniël. What I only learned later was that he had given the identical list to David, since he said that these people would be company for him when I was away screwing somewhere. The only condition on which Daniël insisted was that David did not show me his list. These people, Daniël explained, were very close friends of his, who would not appreciate being brought into contact with anybody as notorious as The Happy Hooker. We discovered his practical joke when we were both about to call the same guy, and compared the two lists. In fact, David had one name which was missing from mine, a certain Julius. Why hadn't Daniël passed me that name? I was curious and determined to encounter the mysterious Julius. I asked David what he knew about him and whether he was an important person. David answered that he had known of Julius for many years, and that he had done more than any man to change the face of Rome. I insisted, and eventually David yielded. Before we left Rome, he would take me to see Julius.

Our hotel, unlike the one in Vienna, made no pretence at being quiet and secluded. It was just off the Via Veneto, one of those streets where, according to local legend, if you sat at the table on the terrace of any of the myriad cafés, sipping your coffee and watching the world pass by, sooner or later you would meet all your friends and acquaintances, no matter in what country they lived. It certainly was a bustling, friendly place. Walking round Rome, I was struck by the great beauty of the ancient, male statues. I had often admired statues in other cities, but they had celebrated female beauty, and it was not until I came to Rome that I found men sculpted in marble with such fantastic power that they really turned me on. Again, there were groups of figures on the Renaissance fountains with strong torsos and wonderful muscles. It came as a surprise to find that my ideal of sexy manhood had been realized in stone, four hundred years ago.

That impression was strongly in my mind when I met Pietro, an accomplished playboy, according to Daniël.

David particularly wanted to spend a day outside Rome, and see the fabulous fountains of the Villa d'Este at Tivoli, which gave me the opportunity to investigate the Roman male in his habitat.

I was not disappointed. Pietro was a very good-looking man indeed, in his mid-fifties, dark, smartly dressed and with the faultless manners of a prince or a duke in the era of Raphael and Michelangelo. He greeted me cordially, fed me impeccably, and in a remarkably short space of time, we were in bed. Like everything else about him, his love-making left nothing to be desired in polish and technical accomplishment. He had a splendid, large cock, but what I admired most were the rippling muscles all over his body, which called to mind those great statues. I was well pleased with my session with Pietro. Of course, he was no longer in the first flush of youth, but his experience showed in everything he did, or rather in the way he did everything. He was just a little bit too perfect, too skilful, and I found myself thinking of him not as Mr Playboy but as Mr Playman. He had seen it all before, but I did not have to make the effort of showing him his way around, and he was gentle and considerate in the way he treated me.

Afterwards, when we were chatting. I told him that I was thinking of taking a trip to Brazil. It turned out that he knew the country well and had a lot of friends there, so he gave me some names which proved to be very useful a few months later.

For some reason, my encounter with Pietro made me keener than ever to meet the legendary Julius, and I suggested to David that we invite him to call on us, but he repeated that I would have to wait. Julius did not get around much these days, he informed me.

Not that I was short of company. The next evening we

struck up a conversation with an intriguing man, named Mario, in our hotel bar. He took an instant liking to us, and invited us home. He lived in a graceful villa which stood amid gardens on a hillside in a fashionable suburb of Rome. The rooms were furnished with immaculate taste, but we spent the time on the terrace, overlooking the city, where we were served with cocktails followed by a virtual banquet.

Mario was a short man, in his late forties, quite bald with lively eyes and rapid hand movements, the sort of man who was accustomed to summing up situations rapidly, and taking decisions without hesitation. He was neat and really quite attractive, but he was direct to the point of abruptness.

I had barely sat down when he scrutinized me and asked, 'Do you trust me?'

I was taken by surprise, but immediately replied, 'No. I like you, but as yet I do not know you, so I cannot trust you.'

The answer pleased him. Apparently, if I had been weak-minded enough to have given him my trust on such slight acquaintance, he would have written me off as being too stupid to be worth cultivating, and he certainly would not have approved if he had thought that I had been trying to flatter him. It was not long before I had good reason to trust him. He was in the diamond business and had a lot of contacts in Israel. When I went to that country, he put me up in his own house there, and was a charming and hospitable host.

In her own way his Swedish mistress, Isabella, was equally remarkable. A tall, handsome blonde, she was the perfect hostess. Everything in the house was in its place, and she appeared to run the place without making the slightest effort. That she was utterly devoted to

Mario was obvious, and we learned that she had left her own husband and their two children in order to be near the man she loved. Mario himself, however, had remained with his own wife, and Isabella enjoyed his company only at weekends, and she was never introduced by Mario to his friends. Yet she accepted the situation without complaint, content to be able to give pleasure to her man.

I happened to mention the Viennese police dog which had amused us at the airport, and Mario told us what had occurred when a similar canine sleuth was brought into the Leonardo da Vinci airport at Rome. The animal was a celebrity, and its arrival was heralded in all the newspapers, just as if it were a world-famous, international footballer up for transfer. God knows how much the Italian authorities paid to sign up this talent! The day that this famous nose went on duty, it was virtually ceremonially unveiled before representatives of the press, and all the officials were watching when the first baggage began to roll up on the conveyor. Suddenly the dog went wild, barking furiously at one suitcase. The unfortunate owner was seized and roughly handled while his case was opened. Inside was an enormous box of chocolates. In no time, the underworld rejoiced in the knowledge that, although the dog had a nose for drugs, it preferred candy. Anyone shipping in drugs made sure to send another case, full of bars of chocolate, by the same plane. After a few weeks, the police decided to write off their investment and the dog was retired, presumably on half-pay, and things returned to normal.

Mario wanted to know what I thought of Rome. I considered and said, 'Like every other city I have visited, it is the people who count far more than the great monuments or the smart shops. It amazes me the way wherever I go folk from my past keep turning up.'

I said this because one evening, back in the hotel, I had been rung up by a girl who had heard that I was in town and had tracked down my number. Jenny used to work for me in New York, and I was delighted to hear from her. David readily agreed that we should invite her for dinner. Jenny was working in Rome, and wanted to know whether our meeting would be business or pleasure.

'What's that supposed to mean?' David asked moodily, when I repeated her question.

'This girl is terrific. Her face is nothing to rave about, but she has the biggest clitoris I have ever come across. She's practically a man, and she is the only woman I have ever paid in my life. So, do we tell her it's a business engagement?'

'And what will the action be tonight?' David asked suspiciously.

'Well, I suppose that she and I will do something: you can pay and watch us.'

David's reply was unrepeatable; I hastened to inform Jenny that she was not being invited to appear professionally.

'In that case,' she replied, 'can I bring a friend?'

It was a strange gathering in the pretty little restaurant, resplendent with red and white checked tablecloths and napkins, so respectable and bourgeois that the head waiter was wearing a stiff shirt. There was David, noticeably ill at ease, sitting beside Jenny, one of my star performers when I ran the most successful house in New York, and on his other side, beaming encouragement to him, sat Giselle, her present employer. We gossiped about business and David was rather left out of things, but Giselle, a plump, pleasant-looking woman, would occasionally pat his hand reassuringly. She casually wrote down her phone number and passed it to him, but I managed to intercept it, and told him that he could have it only if he behaved himself.

'The girls who work for Giselle are the lucky ones,' Mario commented, when I described our dinner party. 'Rome is a magnet which attracts perhaps a thousand girls a day. They come in from the villages and sometimes other towns or even other countries, hoping to make their fortunes as movie stars. They find some cheap pensione, and then try to make contact with film people. What they don't know is that men have been standing at the railway stations, watching for naïve girls, and they have been followed. A few days later they meet by chance, in a café or a bar, a friendly guy who stands them a drink and then, miraculously, turns out to have friends in the film business. So, some poor star-struck kid will be told that she is very pretty, and maybe the kind stranger can help. Sure enough, a big limousine drives up, after a day or two, and she is whisked away to a great country house where she is interviewed by some important-looking men. One of them offers to become her agent and, in no time, she has been persuaded to part with her savings for screen tests. Of course, the house and the car were all hired, and once they have her money, her benefactors usually disappear. Occasionally, there is a screen test of a kind, if the girl is exceptionally pretty. She will be requested to remove her clothes and some film will be shot. She may be kept in the country for a week or more, during which time she will be expected to satisfy the sexual demands of the men, and perhaps of some women who want to "have" her. She will endure being whipped and will have to perform with animals and all sorts of paraphernalia will be used on these sets. The wise ones slink back to their villages; others hold on to their illusions, and end up on the streets as prostitutes, usually falling in love with smooth-talking pimps who take away their passports and threaten to disfigure them if they try to get away. Then there are girls who are shipped out to Arab countries and are often never heard of again.'

That was one aspect of La Dolce Vita which I had not appreciated. But when Mario told me that the fun had gone out of Roman life, and there was merely a terrifying degree of violence where previously there had been joy, I could not entirely agree with him.

The previous night, David and I had gone to an elegant penthouse apartment in the centre of the city, belonging to Alan, an old friend of mine from New York. He looked great, healthy and sunburnt, and was accompanied by a remarkably beautiful young Vietnamese girl called Jasmin. Her features were quite perfect, and her figure was slight, but totally feminine. She had dark brown eyes which seemed to soften when she smiled. In a strange way, she seemed to combine complete innocence with sexual awareness. She breathed seduction, and I noticed that David, who had been suffering from a mild stomach upset, made a miraculous recovery at the sight of this divine apparition.

After dinner, we were sitting talking, but I sensed that Jasmin was distracted and not taking much part in the conversation. I had been flirting mildly with Alan, when Jasmin abruptly left the room. We thought that this would be an appropriate moment for us to depart, but Alan asked me if I would have a word in private with Jasmin. When I spoke to her, the young girl told me, in a roundabout way, that she would like to make love to me. I had thought that she had taken exception to my flirting with Alan, but she was merely shy. She assured me that Alan would not object, and would probably join us. David seemed to be very nice, and would be most welcome if he cared to participate in a mini-orgy. I gazed at her pretty face and slender body, and told myself that there could be no better way of rounding off a perfect evening.

I followed Jasmin into the bathroom. It was decorated in lilac and in the centre stood a heart-shaped tub. Dark purple and pink towels hung from golden bars. Jasmin ran the water and poured in some bath-salts. As she stood in the tub, I hugged her, inhaling her natural odours; then I joined her in the water. Very gently, I soaped her glistening body and her almond-shaped eyes were half closed in pleasure. When I carefully inserted my finger in her tiny asshole, she moaned and seemed to be floating away in rapture. But she was not content simply to be passive. She rubbed my breasts with some aromatic soap in slow, sensual, circular movements. While we were attending to each other, the two men had stolen into the room and removed their clothes. Alan stroked one of Jasmin's sweet breasts with one hand, and with the other cupped one of mine. David had a massive erection and, standing behind Jasmin, caressed her neck and shoulders. She had skin as pale and fragile as precious porcelain, and her long black hair streamed out behind her, accentuating the beauty of her slender, swan-like neck. My Jasmin was a dream of oriental loveliness. I could have looked at her for ever, but her body was trembling eagerly, and I knelt between her legs and lifted her so that her shoulders were above mine. She was as light as air. I kissed and sucked her pussy and her swollen clit. She was making quiet sobbing sounds, which turned me on more than ever as I moved my tongue faster and faster. Both the men had cocks as stiff as ramrods, and while she concentrated on me, holding my head firmly between her hands, Alan's

70

cock was pushing in her ear, and David rubbed his against her neck. Jasmin was pushing my head down as though to force me inside her cunt, and then she came with a soft gasp, and I felt her pubic lips and her big clitoris explode into violent, spasmodic movements against the tip of my tongue.

I was so excited myself that my own clitoris was aching for relief, but a change of scene was necessary. So I towelled and perfumed her, and she led me into the bedroom. She lay naked on the giant bed and took her turn to satisfy me. She worked on me with hands, mouth and her whole body, with a skill which took my breath away. She gave me a fabulous massage, lying with her pussy close to my mouth and so we were able to suck each other off and come at the same time.

The two men could not restrain themselves any longer and no sooner had we got our breath back than Alan mounted her, while I sucked David. Her man came in no time at all, and I pushed David towards her and helped him insert his huge cock into her juicy cunt. She was now on her knees, and he took her from behind, clasping her glorious ass and fucking her good and hard.

As for me, I derived such great pleasure from my lady lover that I had no need of cock, so I took delight in watching what was being enacted in front of me. Everybody had been fully satisfied, and Jasmin apologized, saying that it was late and, for some reason, she felt tired. I covered her with a sheet, kissed her forehead and quietly dressed. David had put on his clothes and was waiting for me outside.

That was what went through my mind when I replied to Mario that I was sure that it was still possible to have a good time in Rome.

It was as though he had read my mind, for with a

knowing smile, he murmured, 'Maybe we too can get acquainted more intimately one day.'

I would not have minded an affair with him; he looked virile and passionate, but his mistress was altogether too cool for my liking.

It was time for us to leave, and the next day we were flying back to Amsterdam. Mario called us a cab. Although he had his car outside, he pointed out that driving back on his own, he would be at the mercy of the armed gangs who roamed the streets and attacked motorists when they were waiting at traffic lights. He also warned us that we might have a problem in getting to the airport next day, since there was going to be a strike by cab drivers. We were in luck. I did a deal with a driver of our cab that, for a substantial payment, he would forget to be on strike until after he had picked us up at our hotel and driven us to the airport.

So, next day, we were on our way, when I reproached David. 'You know, you never did get round to taking me to see Julius. Now it is too late.'

'Not at all,' he replied. 'I purposely left time for us to drop in on our way to the airport.'

I did not understand. Here was this guy who, apparently, was too busy to call on us, and we were going to make a casual call, out of the blue.

'I never said that he was too busy,' David retorted. 'I told you that he did not get around much. You'll soon see why.'

I did when the cab stopped outside the church of San Pietro in Vincoli and David led me inside. There, we stood before that stupendous statue of Moses by Michelangelo.

'That,' said David, 'is the tomb of Pope Julius II.

72

Would you go visiting with that amount of marble on top of you? Now, Xaviera, pay your respects to the man who changed the face of Rome and let's be on our way.'

7

From Pillow to Post

It was November in Amsterdam. Since my return from Vienna and Rome, I had been busy with business and pleasure. David had gone back to Marbella and kept in touch with me by phone and letter. I missed having him around; although his letters were amusing, they were no substitute for the days and nights which we had spent together. It was a case of being driven from pillow to post.

Recently, however, David's letters had become less frequent and before long I learned the reason. He had found a new girlfriend. In fact, since he did not believe in doing things by halves, he had acquired two.

Somehow that man managed to make everything he did as incongruous as a Charlie Chaplin walk. He told me how he had gone to a supermarket in the Port to buy a few groceries. It was late afternoon, and there were not many people about. His attention was caught by a beautiful black girl who seemed to be having some difficulty in finding things. Although she was casually dressed in a T-shirt and blue jeans, she had the poise and elegance of a top model – which, in fact, she was. David unaccountably found he had a sudden need for provisions on racks close to where she was standing. He examined with a professional eye the packets of washing powder which were on display. The girl must have recognized him as a local who knew his way round the tiny supermarket.

'Excuse me, Sir,' she said, 'but can you show me where I can find some bleach?'

David was too taken by the sheer beauty of the girl to see the humour, which appealed greatly to me, of a black girl asking to buy bleach. He was naturally as courteous and helpful as ever, and half an hour later she was back in his apartment having a cup of tea, for David was the complete Englishman. He refused to give me a blow by blow account of what followed, but I had no difficulty in visualizing the scene. He had struck lucky, and Doreen was occupying a good part of his days, and an even better part of his nights.

It was some time later that I heard about his second girlfriend, Marianne, but meanwhile he had come across Sally. She had wandered into Alfonso's shop. That would-be Casanova had eyed David's dusky companion with ill-concealed envy, but here was Sally, a girl originally from Martinique and of much the same complexion, although of a very different temperament. Sally was looking for a rich man who would, of course, fall madly in love with her, adore her, worship her, feed her, clothe her and bedeck her with jewels. Even more important, he should introduce her to influential people in show business so that she could become a raving overnight sensation as a song and dance act. Sally was sexy, and pushy to the point of aggressiveness. Her brown eyes shone with determination: she was a girl who was going to get her own way, come what may. She voiced her aspirations to Alfonso, who suggested that she wait in his shop for David, who was out. Alfonso assured her that David knew all the top people in entertainment. She agreed readily, and this gave Alfonso the chance he had been seeking to chat her up. But Sally was intent on getting her clutches on a man who could throw open the doors of fame, and was not going to waste her time on a mere shopkeeper.

David had gone to the airport, where he had seen

Doreen off on a flight to Paris where she was due to model for *Vogue* magazine. On his return, he was surprised, as he prepared to climb out of the car, to be confronted by Sally's breast, peeping out from her unbuttoned blouse.

'I've been waiting for you,' she announced. 'Why don't you invite me upstairs and offer me a drink?'

David considered all the possible responses, and settled for the easiest. 'Why don't you come upstairs and have a drink?' he said.

Within five minutes, Sally had helped herself to a drink, requisitioned the bottle, since she had no vodka at home to entertain her friends, given David a list of new records which he could obtain for her from London, invited herself to dinner, and was ready to get down to serious business.

'You should hear me sing and see me dance.'

David regarded the prospect without enthusiasm.

'Don't a lot of movie stars live in Marbella?'

'Well,' David answered, 'there's Sean Connery, Stewart Granger, Mel Ferrer, Lidia Christian, Deborah Kerr . . .'

Sally interrupted his catalogue. 'You know Sean Connery? Today is Tuesday. By Friday, fix me an audition with him or Stewart Granger.' She sang a few bars.

David reflected that neither of the actors had ever done him any harm, so why commit an act of wanton aggression by dropping Sally on either of them.

'We had better get going: the restaurants are so crowded later,' he proposed tactfully.

Over the meal, Sally told David just how good she was at all physical pursuits.

He regarded her hopelessly. 'OK,' he sighed resignedly, 'would you like to come back to my place?'

'Sorry, I have a headache: I played too much golf today. I'll see you on Friday.'

Sally was not the sort of girl to deliver in advance, but it was with relief that David drove her back to the apartment where she was staying.

'Was that a picture of Xaviera Hollander I saw in your place?' Sally asked, as she got out of the car.

David assented and said that I was a close friend of his.

'She's the sort of person who could help me in my career as well,' Sally pointed out. 'Set up a meeting with her for me.'

'She is not in Marbella, and I don't know when she will be back.'

Friday passed without Sally showing up, and David breathed freely again. Life was back to normal. He cursed Alfonso and asked why the amorous tradesman had inflicted Sally on him.

'Shit, man, she was ready to fuck,' replied Alfonso.

'Do me a favour,' David told him. 'In future, let me find my own girls. I'm quite good at it now. With the sort of help I get from you, I'll end up in a lunatic asylum or a monastery.'

David was not fated to lead an uneventful existence. The next evening he was back in the Play Bach bar, having a nightcap, when he was approached by a man of about his own age, dark, saturnine, badly shaved and rather scruffily dressed.

'Let me buy you a drink,' the stranger proposed. 'I've seen you around with some pretty girls, and I have been told that you are a friend of Xaviera Hollander. Is that right?'

David pleaded guilty on both counts.

'I have a house up in the hills. I'm a Rodriguez.'

'Please to meet you. My name is David.'

77

'No, I'm A Rodriguez,' he repeated.

'Interesting,' David replied, at a loss. 'Antonio Rodriguez? Alfonso Rodriguez?'

'Rodriguez is not my name. I am called Jean-Christophe. Don't you know what it means in Spain to be a Rodriguez?'

David admitted ignorance. The stranger stared at him as if he were a backward pupil, sipped his drink reflectively and explained.

'When a married man takes a girl away for a weekend and is asked to sign the register, you know that he will use the most common name – Smith in England, Dupont on France and in Spain, Rodriguez. So, to be a Rodriguez means that you are married, but your wife is away so you are, as it were, available. Are you a Rodriguez too?'

David considered: I was safely in Amsterdam and Doreen back in Paris. 'I suppose in a manner of speaking, I am.'

'Good,' chuckled Jean-Christophe. 'You see, I have been a trifle too successful as a Rodriguez, and I have three young ladies staying at my house. That is a bit too much for me to handle, and I would be obliged if you would help me out.'

That was how David came to meet Marianne. She was slender, with long brown hair, soft brown eyes and a delicate olive-tinted skin. Her mother was Siamese and her father French, and as David spoke excellent French they got along very well. She had a shyness about her which appealed to David, so he decided to do Jean-Christophe a favour, and invite Marianne to spend a few days or, more to the point, a few nights with him. She was with her friends, but would be free to join him on the coming Friday.

The day before Marianne was due to arrive, David was called by a friend of mine, Larry, who lived in Brussels and was spending a few days in Mijas, not far from Marbella. David invited Larry and his wife, who was with him, to lunch. Larry accepted gladly but made one impassioned appeal to David.

'My wife is a very suspicious woman. If she thought that I had met you through Xaviera, she would give me a hard time. So please don't mention her name: we were introduced by a mutual business acquaintance. Right?'

David agreed, and hid my photograph in case they came back to his apartment. He found Larry's wife, who by coincidence was also called Sally, a tough, domineering woman who kept her amiable husband under close scrutiny and firm control. Nevertheless, the meeting went off smoothly, and neither of my lovers gave any hint that they had ever cast eyes on the notorious Happy Hooker.

On Friday, David went to collect Marianne. He had gone to great pains to arrange his charming apartment tastefully. There were flowers to welcome her, and waiting in the fridge were vintage champagne and beluga caviar. He even told me that he had spent time rereading some of my books to ensure that he had not forgotten anything, but maybe he had a guilty conscience and wanted to appease me.

When David spread his gastronomic offering before his beloved, the setting was perfect. Candles flickered, the moon hung low over the calm sea, and a romantic Chopin nocturne played softly in the background. But Marianne hardly ate or drank anything, and when David asked if anything was the matter, she replied that she felt a trifle feverish, as if she were developing a heavy cold. He was disappointed, but there was always tomorrow, so he gave her an aspirin and a hot drink and tucked her into bed.

It was two in the morning. Marianne was tossing restlessly in her sleep when the phone rang shrilly. David hurriedly snatched it up.

The voice of an angry woman shouted at him, 'Where the hell is your friend, Xaviera?'

'What?' David was still half asleep. 'Who is that?'

'This is Sally, remember? Now, don't piss about. Where is she?'

David's mind raced. Poor Larry was probably being stretched on the rack, or boiled in oil until he was a delicate shade of golden brown. But after all their precautions, how had Sally discovered their secret, and what should he tell the dreadful woman?

'Oh, you mean that Xaviera,' he suggested weakly.

'Of course I mean that Xaviera. How many Xavieras do you know?'

That was a good question to which he could not think of an effective answer. So he told Sally that I was in Amsterdam, but she retorted furiously that she knew I was in Marbella. David was puzzled: he was certain that if I had returned to Spain, I would have let him know. He looked anxiously at Marianne, who was groaning softly in her fitful sleep.

'Do we have to discuss this now?' he pleaded. 'I have a sick girl with me, and I don't want her to be disturbed.'

'I don't give a shit who you have in bed with you,' Sally insisted. 'This is important, and I want the truth. I have seen a picture of Xaviera in a piano bar in the Port, in a local newspaper.'

David recalled the photograph. It had been taken months ago, but it took him some time to convince Sally.

'Just you remember,' she rapped out, 'the moment you

are in touch with your friend, Xaviera, I want to see her.'
She slammed down the phone.

When David called me, he was still livid with anger
over Sally's lack of consideration, and I assured him that
I would talk to Larry. Meanwhile, he had other worries,
since Marianne's fever turned out to be more serious than
they had thought, and the girl was admitted to hospital,
where David visited her every day.

A week or so later, he called me in Amsterdam and
told me that he had just heard from Larry. After I had
passed on David's complaint, Larry had confronted his
wife, and demanded to know why she had plagued David
in the middle of the night. Sally denied ever having
made the call, and the two of them had a flaming row.
Of course, my involvement with Larry was no longer a
secret.

'The trouble is,' David continued in a subdued voice,
'it's true, she never made that call. This evening, I was in
the middle of Marbella, on my way to the hospital, when
I heard somebody shout to me to give her a lift. There
was this ghastly girl who had wanted me to fix her
auditions with everybody. She was still ordering me
about, and I liked her even less than when we first met.
She wanted me to drop her at the Port. I explained that I
was going to the hospital, which is in the opposite
direction. She had the nerve to ask me to turn round and
drive her to the Port first. I refused: "I go my way, you
go yours," I told her. She turned on her heel and called
over her shoulder, "By the way, sorry to have disturbed
your girlfriend the other night." That was when I realized
that I had blamed the wrong Sally.'

Poor David! Doreen was in Paris and Marianne sick in
hospital. In Amsterdam, I was too far away to afford him

any physical comfort. And to add to his woes, he was stricken with guilt at having been the cause of Larry being persecuted by his Sally: the best he could offer was to officiate as the best man at their divorce.

8

L'Apostrophe

A few days after my conversation with David, I flew to Paris where I was met by Denis, a good friend of mine, who was a steward on Air France. He was a magnificent specimen of manhood, being six feet tall, quite handsome, and one great mass of muscles. His physique was much more developed than usual for a man of twenty-nine, for Denis was into body building in a big way. Indeed, only a week before my arrival, he had won the title of Mr France.

I got the strangest sensation when I slept with Denis because his body was absolutely hairless. Denis explained that the contestants in the Mr France competition were obliged to shave their bodies in order to display their muscles to best advantage. He was not particularly intelligent, but if his brain was not outstandingly talented, his cock was. When we went to bed together, I was agreeably surprised to find that he knew exactly what to do with his hands, his mouth and, last but not least, his beautifully shaped junior. In a very short space of time, I enjoyed several orgasms. We kept conversation to a minimum, and the only in-depth research I encouraged him to undertake was within my body. I adored letting my head rest against that superb chest and feeling his fingers creep slowly over my back, and I experienced a delicious tickling from the short stubble of his hair, which was beginning to grow back. Before I allowed him to penetrate me, I made him give me an exhibition of all the things he could do with that great hunk of body.

He stood there, stark naked, and slowly took in a deep breath. It was amazing to see him expand his arms, shoulders and back, until they appeared to have been inflated to twice their normal size. It was as though his flesh and blood had been turned into iron, and his waist looked tiny in comparison with that huge thorax. Then he took up various poses, some of which were very sexy. He had a fascinating way of flexing the muscles on the left and right sides of his chest independently of each other. I could not help thinking that if he had tassels on his nipples, he would have made a terrific stripper. The mere sight of those great coiling sinews was a tremendous turn-on.

They were not only great to look at. When he was inside me, I could feel the muscles of his buttocks tighten under my hands, and looking at his massive arms while he pumped up and down on top of me I had to concede that there was something to be said for body building. Then, just before he reached his climax, a tiny tremor would run through the tendons of his neck, and the veins would swell and stand right out of his forehead. His face would assume an intense expression, and as he shot his load he would roar like an infuriated bull.

That afternoon we both came several times, and afterwards it was comforting to fall asleep in those strong arms. Normally, I like to sleep on my own, but with Denis I curled up and made myself small, totally protected by him. He kept himself in strict training: I suppose if he had let himself go, he would have deteriorated into a great flabby dumpling in no time.

Denis did a lot to make my stay in Paris easy. He loved serving people, a definite attribute in a steward, and he had become my slave, desiring nothing more than to look after me, run errands for me or drive me wherever I might want to go. Like many strong men, he was extremely gentle and good-tempered. It made me feel good to know that his keen, green eyes were always alert, watching out for any danger that might threaten me.

What had brought me to Paris this time was an invitation to appear in a TV programme, called *L'Apostrophe*. But first I took the opportunity to do some shopping and to dine in some of the world's finest restaurants with a few friends. Best of all was simply enjoying Paris in autumn, particularly the Latin Quarter. I would stroll down the Boulevard St Germain and pause for a coffee at Les Deux Magots or the Café Flore and watch the world go past. They were the haunts of celebrities who have long since departed, but there was always something going on. Tourists, hugging their cameras, would jostle with long-haired students who seemed perpetually to be discussing the political situation, and the pavements were crowded with shoppers and window shoppers. I watched a couple who acted out a mime, imitating the stilted movements of dolls, reminding me that this was the city of Marcel Marceau. It is impossible to be bored in Paris.

I made a point of going to a branch of Fnac, a sort of cultural supermarket where you can choose from an enormous array of books, records, photographic equipment and similar goodies. The shop is so popular that there is always a line of people waiting to get in when it opens, and the check-outs are as busy as those at a grocery store. I bought a lot of records of all sorts of music for myself, and I got a kick out of finding some really out-of-the-way works for David which I knew he would appreciate in the musical wilderness of Marbella. I was especially pleased to find a number of 'Music Minus One' discs of piano concertos and chamber music where the piano part is left out of the recording, so that David and other enthusiasts can play the music to the accompaniment of the recording. David was due to come to Paris in time for my TV show, and I was looking forward to giving him his presents. But I was to be disappointed. That evening, he phoned me at my hotel.

'I've got a lot of trouble here, Xaviera,' he said. 'There's been a traffic accident: I hit a woman who has since died. The police are satisfied that it was not my fault, but I won't be able to leave Spain until they have completed some formalities.'

He explained that, as a foreigner, he would be obliged to pay a sum into the court or put up a bail bond to cover any damages that might be awarded, if a case were to be brought by the dead woman's relatives, and until a judge had fixed the amount and David had paid the cash or arranged the bond, he was obliged to surrender his passport.

I must admit that my first reaction was not sympathy for the victim, but concern for any damage that his beautiful, gleaming Rolls might have sustained. I remembered how, during the summer when David was indoors working, I would cruise in that most dignified vehicle with the hood down, and how every head would turn in my direction. I pulled myself together.

'When will you be able to come, then?'

He answered, 'That's difficult to say. In fact I have made all the necessary arrangements for the bond with my bank. They are examining the documents, and they only have to give their guarantee to the court, but their legal department never seems to be ready. Every day when I go to the bank and ask whether they have the OK from their legal department the manager looks through the post and says, "Not yet, it will be in tomorrow," so

86

I'm expecting to come any time, but each day I've had the same experience. I'm very sorry. I would have liked to see your show, but I don't think I'll be able to make it.'

David hesitated; there was obviously something else on his mind as well. Eventually he said to me, 'Well you see, not only was I going to meet you in Paris, but I think you ought to know that of course Doreen lives in Paris, and she's expecting to see me as well. By the way, do you remember I mentioned this little girl who had been staying with me for a while? Well it so happens that she's in Paris too and so I must say I was looking forward to rather a busy week. I find it difficult to get hold of them because well, you know what Spanish telephones are like!'

I did know what Spanish telephones were like, and I even had some sympathy with David in his predicament although I must admit the situation had its humorous side.

'Well, can I help you in any way?' I said. 'Would you like me to talk to the other two girls?'

'No!' said David very definitely.

That made me quite definite in my mind that I would like to talk to the girls.

'Come on,' I coaxed. 'They must know of my existence.'

'The whole world knows of your existence. I don't want you fouling up what has been a most satisfactory relationship with two sweet young ladies,' he protested.

'Now, what would give you that sort of idea? I only want to help.'

The conversation went on for some time, but ultimately David agreed reluctantly, since he could not be sure of getting through himself, to give me their numbers.

'What's more,' I cooed, 'I'll invite them to the show, and perhaps we can get together and have a little dinner afterwards. I am sure that we must have a lot to discuss: you will be present in spirit.'

I did not catch David's reply, but I got the impression that he was not the most contented man in Spain. Although I had a lot to do by way of preparation for the programme, I found the time to call the two girls. I gave Marianne a brief account of David's accident, and assured her that he was unhurt. She replied immediately,

'How is the car?'

I had to chuckle. It was obvious that this young lady and I had more than one thing in common. She said that she would try to get to the show, but could not be sure that she would be able to make it. In any case, she promised that she would meet me later in the lobby of the George V.

Doreen's reaction was totally different. I started to tell her about the accident, but she interrupted me and asked in a voice full of concern, 'What about David? Is he all right?'

Once I had reassured her, she became very collected. When I invited her to come to the studio for the TV show, she had to consult her diary before accepting.

'That will be fine,' she confirmed. 'I shall be able to fit that in. I am very much looking forward to meeting you, Miss Hollander, or may I call you Xaviera?'

I could not help fantasizing what these two girls would look like from their voices, and I was curious to see how David's taste had developed. But I had to hurry to get my act together in order to meet my faithful Denis on time for him to get me to the studio.

I had already met the other members of the panel, since the previous day the TV station had arranged a session for reporters and photographers, and we had been interviewed on radio. There were two other women and two men: I was the only foreigner. One of the women, Christine Desforges, a redhead with a lot of sex appeal, struck me as both sympathetic and bright. She had written a number of erotic books, but her main activity was running the publishing company which she had formed. The other woman was a very different person. Prudish, fifty-odd, she had written a book called *The Velvet Male*, a title to which I took an instant dislike. Her sexual fantasy had been committed to print after thirty years of quiet, uneventful marriage. I could not wait for the end of the broadcast, as I had other interviews arranged, so I left directly after my part of the programme was over. However, I listened to the rest on the radio in the car, and I was infuriated to hear the older woman launch a fierce attack on me and my books. She denounced them as mere sex guides, without any trace of romance or love. I resolved to get my own back when we were before the TV cameras. That evening I scanned the books of the other people on the show, but I paid particular attention to hers. It was the most boring and trivial rubbish, and after a few pages I threw it aside.

L'Apostrophe is an important series, noted for its high quality and intellectual tone. It is broadcast nationwide, and enjoys a large following, so I could be sure that there would be millions of viewers watching when we appeared. The subject for discussion was whether there was any difference between pornography and eroticism, and the role of both in literature. I had taken part in many open-line radio programmes in the USA and Canada, and while facile compliments would leave me unmoved, whenever some spiteful old woman attacked me, my hair would bristle, the adrenaline would flow and I would be ready with a stinging retort. And tonight, I was in top form.

Because of the heavy traffic I was a little late getting to the studio, and when I arrived, there were dozens of people already there. I was rushed into the make-up room, and the last dab of powder had hardly been applied before photographers were popping flash-bulbs and we were ushered to the podium. I had no chance to try to identify Doreen, or look out for any of my own friends whom I had invited.

The men on the panel were Michel Girodias, the title of whose book *J'Arrive*, I am coming, has the same double meaning in French as in English, and Michel Gall, who had written a book about the sex life of Robinson Crusoe which sounded very funny. There was a literary critic who interviewed and predictably brought up authors like Apollinaire, and such current favourites as Emmanuelle Arsan's *Emmanuelle* and Pauline Réage's *The Story of O*. As my own books had been rated by different critics as everything from dirty to educational, I felt qualified to pass judgement on the work of others, and, fortunately, my French is fluent enough for me to give a good account of myself. I was asked point-blank how I distinguished between pornography and erotic literature, to which I replied that, since the French were noted for their understanding of wine, it was the same as the difference between a common table wine and Château Lafite. There were the inevitable references to D. H. Lawrence and *Lady Chatterley's Lover*, Henry Miller and Beaudelaire and we got to Erica Jong's *Fear of Flying*, by way of the Marquis de Sade. I gave my opinion that pornography makes a statement whereas eroticism makes a suggestion, and this was logical since eroticism aims to excite where pornography merely shocks.

It was when the discussion became general that my chance came. My adversary was rash enough to repeat her attack on me, but I interrupted her.

'Yes, we heard all that yesterday on the radio, and you are not saying anything which has not been served up before. But to say that there is no love in my books is absurd. Of course there is also sex, but what is wrong with that? There's plenty of sex in life, isn't there? And I am not ashamed either of the educational content of my books, which has been praised by literary critics as well as sociologists. But having attempted to read your own book, I can understand your bitterness, for it is utterly devoid of love or any other emotion, and is consequently completely sexless. Indeed, it does not seem to me to have any content whatsoever.'

She had not expected this onslaught, and was stopped dead in her tracks. I was gratified that in the debate which ensued, the other speakers contributed to the crushing of her pretensions. By the time the show was over, I was more than satisfied with the outcome of our encounter. Once again, there were the hordes of reporters, commentators, critics and various artists, all the hundreds of people who always seem to sprout up out of the ground at the end of a TV show, and each and every one has something to say to you.

Finally, exhausted but happy, I was able to slip away, and Denis drove me back to the George V, where I was to face my second adventure of the evening.

9

When Shall We Three Meet Again?

My faithful chauffeur-factotum stopped the car outside the impressive entrance to the Hotel George V, and I strode into what I consider to be the most splendid lobby in Europe. I always get a thrill when the uniformed porter holds open the massive front doors, and I sweep inside to be confronted by the fine paintings and bronzes, the rich tapestries, antique furniture and superb carpets. No matter at what hour of the day or night one arrives, there is always a great throng of people, coming and going, and this night was no exception. The entrance lobby is joined to the bar by a corridor which is really another salon, for it is spacious and lined with comfortable armchairs, above which are hung valuable paintings in heavy gilt frames.

Although there were lots of people sitting and talking or waiting for friends, I had no difficulty in picking out Doreen. She was tall, probably not far short of six feet, and into my mind there flashed the fantastic vision of David making love to her, standing on a box. Should short men go with tall women? Napoleon seemed to make out all right, but would his example be much of an inspiration for David?

Doreen rose to greet me. She had a stately beauty which commanded admiration. Her shiny black hair was swept back, her make-up impeccable, and the satin sheen of her skin was perfectly set off by the blouse which she was wearing. It was a rich tone of brown and it harmonized unexpectedly with the bronze of her flesh. David had told me that she was a friend of Yves St Laurent, for whom she worked, and I presumed that he was the source of that lovely garment, but Doreen assured me that it was actually a shirt which she had brought back from New York. She certainly knew how to dress.

When I asked her if she had been waiting long, she recounted how she had been sitting close to a large potted palm tree when she heard a noise.

'There was this disagreeable-looking man, skulking behind the palm tree, eyeing me most suggestively and going "pssst". He was positively leering at me.' Doreen regarded me coldly and went on. 'I suppose there must be quite a few hookers hanging round the hotel, trying to pick men up. But I was not happy that this miserable creature should mistake me for a prostitute.'

'Perhaps he didn't,' I ventured. 'Maybe he just wanted to date you.'

Doreen reflected and smiled faintly. 'A date under a palm tree? Well, I did not approve of him. I stood up and looked down at him. "Sir," I said, "I am not in the habit of speaking to strange men in the lobbies of hotels. If, by any chance, I made an exception to this rule, it would not be for some slimy little toad who hissed at me from behind a potted palm."'

I grinned. 'So what did he say?'

'Nothing. He just fled.'

'A pity,' I laughed. 'You might at least have found out how much he was prepared to offer.'

Doreen clearly did not consider my reaction to the intruder favourably, but before she could comment, we were interrupted by the arrival of Marianne. I had seen her enter the hotel from the corner of my eye, but, of course, I did not know who she was. She had been accompanied by a young man whom she fondly kissed goodnight. She must have recognized me from photographs, and walked over to where we were sitting.

When I had first set eyes on Doreen, I had been impressed by her statuesque beauty: she was majestic, and a truly mature woman. But Marianne astounded me. David had never bothered to mention to me that his latest love was a girl of about eighteen. Good God, I thought, he's entered his second childhood, and, by the look of her, he must be enjoying every minute of it. Marianne had a slender but sinuous figure and her breasts were full and well developed. She had an oval face, beautifully regular features, and her skin was of that delicate shade so typical of lovely Eurasians: it was a perfect setting for her soulful brown eyes. David had found himself two wonderfully attractive women, but how different they were!

'Why don't we go up to my suite?' I suggested. 'We can order sandwiches and something to drink. Then we can chat in comfort.'

When we were settled upstairs, Marianne sipping a gin and tonic, Doreen and I with fruit juices, I asked if they had seen the show. Marianne said apologetically that she had wanted to get out, but that there had been so many things to do that she had not been able to make it, and that her TV was not working, but asked me to tell her all about it. Doreen had been at the studio, and she congratulated me on the way I had disposed of my tiresome opponent. Marianne did not strike me as the sort of girl who would spend her evening at home reading books, but Doreen demanded if I meant what I had said during the programme about the distinction between eroticism and pornography. I did not want to get involved in another heavy discussion; one an evening seemed sufficient, but Doreen was serious and deserved some sort of answer.

'Yes, I think so,' I replied pensively. 'But maybe erotic literature is simply pornography with an intellectual alibi.'

I switched the subject to what the two girls were doing in Paris. To my surprise, Marianne was a student at the Sorbonne, studying French language and literature. However, I was by no means sure that was how she really spent her time. Doreen was a much more earnest person. In addition to her work as a model, she was doing a course in beauty culture, and she hoped eventually to establish herself as a cosmetologist, either in France or in New York. I noticed that when Doreen started asking me about my life and my books, Marianne looked interested. But there was something in her expression which convinced me that her mind was less on an intellectual discussion than on something considerably more physical. Inevitably, the conversation naturally turned to David.

I wanted to play down his accident. 'You know he is really one of the most clumsy people I have ever met. He's clumsy with his hands and feet, and it seems that he is just as clumsy with his car.'

Marianne's eyes twinkled, and she murmured that there was one part of his body with which he was not clumsy at all, but Doreen sprang to his defence.

'That's not fair,' she protested. 'How can you say that his hands are clumsy? Have you watched him play the piano? I love watching his fingers moving over the keyboard.'

I realized that Doreen was deeply in love with him, and she was definitely the most romantically inclined of the three of us.

'Yes, you are right,' I conceded. 'I have told him that his hands and his cock are his most beautiful features.'

I wanted to see how they would react, but neither of them rose to the bait, although I had noted Marianne's earlier remark. However, she confined her comments to his prowess at the piano.

'I like his playing too, but sometimes I wish he would stop and take me out dancing instead.'

Doreen flared up. 'Do you really love him?'

'Yes I do, though perhaps not in the same way that you do.' The young girl had suddenly become very serious. 'He is kind and gentle, and he has been very good to me.'

'But you hardly know him,' I rejoined. 'And I thought that you looked rather attached to that young man when you came into the hotel.'

Marianne gazed at me steadily. 'I have not known David quite as long as you have, but I have seen enough of him to be able to form my own opinion. As for the boy downstairs, he is my French boyfriend, David is my Spanish boyfriend, and, if you are interested, I have boyfriends in quite a few other places as well. But I am sure that you do not find that shocking, Xaviera. Have you been completely faithful to David?'

I realized that, young as Marianne was, I was not dealing with a child, and I found myself believing that she did sincerely love David in her own fashion, although Doreen was clearly unconvinced. We talked tenderly of David, when an unexpected difference between our recollections of him emerged.

Doreen had said how much she liked his silver-grey hair. 'But his hair could look even better.' She glared at us imperiously. 'There are still a few strands of a rather nondescript brown. I told him that he ought to dye it all white: he would look so distinguished. You know he agreed at once.'

'Well, that's strange,' I observed. 'I told David about a girlfriend of mine who had competely shaved her head and how sexy it was. She is quite bald, and the sight of her really sets me going. When I asked him, he said that of course he would shave his head to please me.'

It was Marianne who had the last word. 'I was with him after either of you, and I can assure you that he is neither bald nor snowy white. Actually, I pointed out that if he dyed his hair its original colour, he would look twenty years younger. He promised that he would dye it black.'

But I think that we all three knew that David was so good-natured that he would promise all of us whatever we demanded, but that he had not the slightest intention of doing anything about it. Perhaps our absent friend had the laugh on us. As we discussed his foibles, we grew quite sentimental.

'Poor David,' I murmured. 'What a pity he isn't here with the women who love him.'

'I wonder where he is now,' Marianne said. Her eyes were misty with tears.

We sat in silence, each of us recalling tender moments we had enjoyed with the man who had come to mean so much to us. Our reverie was disturbed by a timid knock. I walked over and unlocked the door. There, on the threshold, holding a small travelling bag and looking very dishevelled, was David. We women gazed at each other in astonishment, and we turned to him, but I was the one who broke the spell.

'What the hell are you doing here?' I demanded.

'That's not much of a welcome,' David complained. 'Aren't you even going to ask me in?'

I waved him to a chair. 'We have been wasting our sympathy on you, thinking of you languishing in Spain, far from your nearest and dearest – well your dearest anyway. You are supposed to be alone and miserable, and you have the nerve to walk into my hotel room. What do you think that you are doing?'

'Xaviera is right,' Marianne interposed. 'You make up

all those excuses about not being able to come to Paris, and then you arrive without a word of warning.'

'Look, I have just managed to get my passport, and I rushed to Paris to be with you,' David said indignantly. 'It's not as though I have been with anybody else. I knew that Xaviera stayed at the George V, so I came straight here. Aren't you pleased to see me?'

The amazing thing was that I don't think we were. All three of us were in love with the same man, sympathizing with him in his absence, and then he was so inconsiderate as to turn up and spoil our sentimental scene.

'This is too much,' Marianne scolded. 'You have no sense of what is decent behaviour. I'm going home. Goodnight, everybody.'

As she stalked out of the room, I could not help wondering whether she had not made a date with the young man who had brought her to the hotel. After all, she had told us that he was her Paris lover.

As for Doreen, who had defended David so stoutly against our criticisms, she got to her feet. 'It is obvious that you have come to see Xaviera, so I shall leave you alone together.'

David was in a quandary. If he contradicted Doreen, he would risk offending me, and if he agreed with her, he would offend her. So he said nothing. Doreen made a dignified departure.

I turned to David. 'Now, what have you to say for yourself?'

'Well, how I got my passport back is quite a story. In fact, it is a lesson on how to get anything done in Spain. Let me tell you.'

'OK, but make it short. I have had a long day and the TV show was quite a strain. And I am so tired that, please darling, just for tonight, call reception and get yourself another room.'

So, our gallant lover was rejected by all three of his ladies. But, before he retired, he did tell me what had happened to him.

10

In the Spirit of Don Quixote

Despite his promise to be brief, David obviously was savouring the opportunity to tell me his little story, and although I was tired, I was ready to enjoy his anecdote.

'You know,' he began, 'now that summer is over, my apartment gets cold and I have to buy wood for my fire.'

'What has that got to do with your passport?'

'Be patient. We have had a lot of rain, and when I went to the only wood-seller in the area, he just laughed at me. "Of course you want wood," he jeered. "Everybody wants wood, now that winter has set in. But there is no wood. All my stock has been soaked and is unusable."'

'So you slipped him a couple of thousand pesetas and, miraculously, he discovered some dry wood. Right?'

'Wrong,' David countered. 'I was warned some time ago against attempting to bribe Spaniards, or at any rate, Andalucians. An acquaintance of mine who had recently arrived in Spain from Paris went, as a matter of course, to buy the local police chief. To his amazement, he was rebuffed. "We are not a nation of prostitutes, like the French. Spaniards may be poor, but we have our pride," retorted the official.'

'Get to the point,' I yawned.

'Remember our old friend George, the American who has lived so long in Andalucia that he has practically become a native? Well, I ran into him and I told him of my plight. He promised to bring me wood. I was sure that he would never deliver, but I was astonished when a couple of days later George turned up at my place with a truck full of firewood. When I asked him how much I owed him, George scratched his head and told me that the service cost more than the commodity.'

'What was that supposed to mean?'

'I had no idea, but over a cup of coffee, he told me what had happened. George had gone to the wood-seller who had refused me, and met with the same response. "But you don't understand," George persisted, "this is not for me, but for a friend of mine who lives in the Port." The trendy address made the tradesman more determined than ever, but George would not take no for an answer. "My friend has a girl in his apartment, and she is beautiful. She has golden hair, the colour of ripening corn, and her eyes are as blue as the distant ocean. Her voice is sweet music, and her lips are full, moist and tempting." He had captured the wood-seller's attention, and George went into exquisite details on the girl's figure. Her firm, creamy breasts were hillocks of delight, and the swell of her belly and of her hips could drive a man crazy with desire. "And your friend," breathed the wood-seller, "he loves this girl?" "Of course. And she is infatuated with him. They were born to be lovers. The aroma of her sensual body inflames him: he cannot keep his eyes from feasting on her and his arms ache when she is not enfolded within them."'

'Hey,' I interrupted. 'Who is this chick? You have never mentioned her to me, and I bet that neither Doreen nor Marianne has any idea of what is going on.'

David ignored my question. He had a faraway, blissful look on his face, as he contemplated his beloved in his mind's eye, and there was a bulge in his trousers which was more eloquent than his words. With an effort, he pulled himself together and continued. 'The wood-seller could not restrain himself. "Tell me," he urged George.

"How do they make love, this friend of yours and his beautiful girl?" George shook his head sadly. "They do not make love. My poor, frustrated friend cannot persuade her to come to bed because the flat is too cold. If only he could make a fire." He did not have time to finish his sentence. The gallant Andalucian had rushed off, and returned with the first load of wood, perfectly dry, of course. When the truck was full, George asked how much he owed. "I do not want payment," was the scornful reply. "This is for love, and passion is not measured in pesetas. Let your friend make love to his dream woman."'

'That is a very pretty story, but what the hell has it got to do with your passport?'

'Well, I told you that I have been waiting for the bank to finalize their guarantee, so that the court would release my passport. Each day, I have gone to the manager's office, and it was always going to be in the next day's mail. It was the thought of the three of you, sitting here, dissecting me in my absence, and discovering guilty secrets which I did not even remember, that finally spurred me into activity. I recalled George's success with the wood-seller and decided to use the same tactics.

'This morning, I stormed into the manager's office without letting anyone announce me and without knocking. "I must have my passport," I shouted. He was shocked, but gazed at me sympathetically and ruffled through the morning's letters. There was the customary expression of regret and the promise of *mañana*. I insisted that tomorrow would be too late. "But why, Señor, what is the urgency?" I became wild and passionate. "I am in love," I exclaimed. Word for word, I repeated George's touching description of my beloved, and the bank manager was visibly moved. "But, Señor, I do not understand. Why are you not at home, making love to this adorable creature?" My tone was tragic. "She has left me and flown to Paris. If I do not go after her today, I shall have lost her for ever."

'The effect on him was electric. He leaped to his feet, rushed downstairs and told his senior clerk to look after the place while he dealt with vital business for his client. Then he bundled me into his car and drove to the main office of the bank in Marbella. He virtually tore the joint apart, grabbed a typewriter and prepared the form of guarantee himself. Then we went off to the court, and ten minutes later my passport was safely in my hands. I started to thank him, but he cut me short. "It is nothing. I did it for love. Now, go, find your beautiful girl, and make love to her."

'You know, Xaviera, if I had said that I had to go away to make some enormously important financial deal, nothing would have happened. But you can rely on the romantic temperament of the Spaniard – or at least that of the true Andalucian. So, here I am.'

'Very interesting, but it's late and I am going to be busy tomorrow, so off you go, my darling. Goodnight.'

'Are you really going to turn me out?'

I nodded. 'Why don't you go to this paragon of beauty whom you have pursued to Paris? You would not like me to think that you got your passport back on false pretences.'

'I only wish that she existed outside George's imagination,' David complained bitterly, as I pushed him out of the door.

11

The Dutch Connection

David was not able to stay long in Paris, as he had to
return to Spain to deal with the enquiry into his accident,
and what time he did have, he shared between Doreen,
Marianne and myself. He looked really tired when I
kissed him goodbye, but there was a contented smile on
his lips. Of course, I had my faithful Denis, but he could
not be available when he was on duty with Air France. I
was never short of company, but I decided that I would
summon Richard, one of my friends from Amsterdam, to
come and join me for the rest of my stay in Paris. It was
not difficult for me to persuade him to escape to Europe's
sexiest city.

My relationship with Richard was similar to that with
David, inasmuch as we left each other totally free to do
whatever we felt like. However, I had much deeper
emotional feelings towards David: Richard was more of a
buddy with whom I could have a lot of fun and laughter.
He had been married for about seven years and had a six-
year-old daughter, but was now divorced. When I first
met him, he was unemployed. He was very well spoken
and amusing, with a great sense of humour. However, he
could sleep for hours on end, and he was not exactly
aggressive in his pursuit of work. He was very handsome,
with thick black curly hair, a pale complexion and a
general air of shyness. He had studied to be a ballet
dancer but, being absolutely heterosexual, got fed up with
the homosexual attentions which were paid to him, and
decided that the time had come for a change in his way of

life. But it was only after he met me that he got jolted out of a routine of living with his mother, eating, sleeping and chatting. His rather fragile appearance was deceptive. He took me to one of the toughest areas of Amsterdam, where an arm-wrestling contest was to take place. I was surprised when he decided to enter, but he took on all the big, heavy guys, made it to the finals, and ultimately carried off the first prize, a fine silver trophy. So, even when Denis was not around, I had another bodyguard who could protect me – when he was awake.

Sexually, we did not get along all that well, since we had completely different concepts of making love. There are lovers and there are fuckers, and Richard definitely fell into the latter category. For him, a woman was a creature with tits, legs, ass and a hole in the middle which had to be filled. He did not hate women, but he did not respect them either. He simply liked to fuck, preferably straight up and down, in the missionary position. He could not be bothered with any preliminaries, he did not care about getting blown, and he considered eating pussy as something utterly repellent.

For some weeks I attempted to turn him into a more tender lover, but eventually gave it up as hopeless. I remember vividly one occasion, when I returned from a two-month trip to Brazil, and he came to meet me at the airport. He insisted on fucking me in the car, and when I resisted he told me that he felt like a sailor who had been at sea for months without seeing a woman and, whether I liked it or not, he was going to have me there and then. So, right by the side of the motorway, he fucked the hell out of me. I had not experienced anything like it since my high-school days, and I must admit that I soon began to enjoy it. Just occasionally, I believe, every woman finds it quite exciting to be virtually raped, without any of the formalities of foreplay.

As it happened, during this stay in Paris I was able, in a sense, to get even with Richard, for he ended up doing what I wanted when he took part in one of my more flamboyant sex scenes. But, long before that, I had started the process of broadening his outlook. Not that he led a sheltered existence: he was commissioned to do some radio interviews in one of the more colourful areas of Amsterdam, and he swapped yarns with whores and pimps, wrestlers and boxers, pushers and other assorted characters. What gave him a certain naïvety was his choice of friends, who were all either married, or were men living conventionally with a girl. Until he met me, he had no idea of any relationship other than the super-straight. Quite early in our friendship, we went to an after-hours club called Chez Nelly. I began to get a headache, and at about one thirty decided to go home, but Richard was standing at the bar, talking to a pretty young brunette. I did not want to spoil his evening, for like me he is a night person, so I went up to him, pushed twenty-five guilders into his hand, and told him to buy the girl a drink and call me in the morning. He was flabbergasted at the way I practically thrust him into the arms of another woman, without being in the slightest jealous.

In Paris, we took in the Louvre and the Pompidou Centre, since he is keen on cultural activities, as well as going to the Moulin Rouge, where he could go apeshit over the most beautiful women in the world, and the Alcazar, a theatre with transvestite performers, musicians and comics in the old, burlesque style. But these were simply preliminaries: the grand finale of our stay was a party which I organized at the home of a girlfriend of mine. Stephanie was a very sensual lady who, as I have

106

described in one of my earlier books, during the Film Festival at Cannes had no hesitation in fucking half a dozen policemen, practically simultaneously. The world knew her as a sex-loving exhibitionist who had made porno movies and written a book about swinging. She led an ideal life, being kept by a wealthy businessman who lived out of town with his wife and children. From Friday to Monday he stayed with his mistress, and there was always some sort of party going on over the weekend. I had no qualms about taking Richard to an orgy: he was well equipped and, when fucking, had a splendid rhythm, although he lacked tenderness and was definitely short on foreplay. How different he was from David, whose greatest pleasure was to give pleasure.

I told Richard simply that he was going to a special sort of party. He had no idea of what to expect and was stricken with stage fright when I pushed him through the front door and introduced him to Stephanie. She was dressed in an almost see-through kaftan, embroidered with gold flowers and dragons, and leaving little to the imagination as to what she was hiding beneath it. She looked glorious with her golden hair cut short, and her big blue eyes flashed a challenge to Richard. Many people compared her with me: she was an excellent hostess and spoke as many languages as I did, but our characters were diametrically different. There were times I met her outside her natural environment when I simply could not stand her because she would strive to draw everybody's attention to herself and shock the entire world. In her own home, however, she was charming, gracious and thoughtful, never neglecting any of her guests, of whom there was quite a collection.

We entered the lounge and gazed around us. There were men and women everywhere, standing on the balcony, sitting on armchairs and couches, or lying on cushions on the floor. Most of them were still fully dressed, but looking at the women, I saw that each of them had something extravagant about her. One might have an extremely low décolletage, accentuating a huge pair of tits, another would be wearing a beautiful, long, black silk skirt, with a slit on each side which opened all the way up to her buttocks. There was a young woman sitting with her legs wide apart, revealing crotchless lace panties below her short skirt from which a bushy pussy stared up at us. A handsome black guy had shown up in tight-fitting leather trousers from which the ass had been cut out. I suppose most of the people were between twenty-five and forty-five, but some of the young women had escorts whose wealth presumably compensated for their greater age.

I knew that it was not uncommon in France for a rich man in his fifties to get divorced from the wife with whom he had lived for years to remarry a very much younger woman. What he considered a union of love, his new mate saw as a convenient financial arrangement. At this very party, I got talking with just such a couple. André, a friendly if rather unattractive man in his late fifties, had a kind face and a protruding belly. He was with a sexy 25-year-old from Marseilles, who was lovingly caressing a teenage boy. André had been married for almost thirty years when he met Françoise, straight out of a convent, and fell madly in love with her. They had recently got married, and André had so much confidence in Françoise that he had put his house in Antwerp and a fine mansion in St Tropez, where they spent their summers, in her name.

'Listen, Xaviera,' André said. 'I'm not a fool. When I met Françoise, she was an innocent girl whose father had just died. It was natural that she would look for a father figure, but she would also need a sex life. I'm not the most handsome man in the world, and although I have a big cock and can still manage to come once a day, eventually a woman who came to me as a virgin would get bored. So, after we had been together for about three years, I proposed that she should go and find herself a good-looking young man on the beach or in a discotheque and bring him home. I told her that I wanted her to make love to him, but that I would be there, so that I could watch and share her enjoyment. She was startled, but after thinking about it, she agreed, and since then we have been swingers. And, as it happens, Françoise sometimes takes a fancy to a woman, and all three of us will make love. You ought to see the way she dresses up for her audience and then strips. Don't you think that she is a very sensual lady?'

I regarded the girl from the convent, and nodded.

'And you know,' André continued, 'I have discovered that when she brings home some new victim, and I watch a shapely, smooth body fuck my wife, I get a tremendous thrill and I have developed blatant homosexual tendencies. I get a great kick out of sucking her cunt when some young man has just filled it with his love juices. I have got as far as stroking another man's penis, but I am still a bit uptight about taking it in my mouth. However, give me time, I'm still young. But look at Françoise now with that boy: doesn't she look simply radiant? Why don't you go over and play with him as well? You are supposed to be a great expert, and I would love to see the two of you with him. And, while you are about it, don't neglect her: she is as sweet as honey.'

I walked over, and I must say that I approved of André's taste, and, looking at the boy, of Françoise's taste also. I fondled the couple for a moment, but I did not feel in the mood to do what other people wanted, so I wandered around the room to see how my own protégé was getting on. The fun of group sex is for everyone to be in the same room, instead of slipping away to individual bedrooms and fucking on the beds. An hour had elapsed since our arrival, and by now the floor was littered with panties, brassieres, skirts, trousers and shirts.

Stephanie was smoking a cigarette, a long black holder between her fingers. She was seated on a fluffy velvet couch, wearing spiky heels and nylons with a garter belt. She had drawn her legs up, so that her heels rested on the couch. Her kaftan had dropped over her knees, giving a clear view of her crotch to anybody who was on the floor. Richard, aghast by the proceedings, was sitting demurely next to her. I settled down beside him, put my arm around his shoulders, kissed him and asked him if he was enjoying the party.

'I feel such a square. Everybody else is having a great time, but I am not even turned on. Usually I have a hard-on twenty-four hours a day: something must be wrong with me.'

'The women like the look of you: I can tell,' I assured him. 'You surely don't have an inferiority complex, do you?'

He blushed. 'Maybe I have. All the guys look so super, at least the younger ones. It makes me feel inadequate.'

I could understand his misgivings. Stephanie had an outstanding selection. Swingers and nudists are not necessarily handsome, but they are aware of their bodies, and tend to take good care of themselves. There was nobody present who was either grossly overweight or painfully skinny, and nobody was dirty or loud and arrogant. It was a pleasant mixture of rather attractive

110

people. Even the older men, whose role was voyeur, financial supporter or procurer, stayed tactfully in the background. No man forced himself on any girl, and everybody was aware of his or her function.

But Richard presented me with a problem. I had brought along this magnificent stud to display him to my friends, and he had become as timid and shy as a rabbit. I whispered to Stephanie and then crossed the room to watch developments. However, I was not going to be allowed to remain a passive observer. I was seated in a big chair, opposite the couch, when a French scriptwriter whom I knew, a very handsome guy, approached me, and in no time at all he had stripped off my panties from underneath my dress. He slipped off my shoes, and began slowly sucking my toes. I got an exquisite feeling and my nipples instantly popped up. But my eyes were fixed on Stephanie, who had pulled Richard on to the floor in front of her.

Suddenly, he cried out, 'My God, a naked pussy! How wonderful, a shaved cunt! I've never seen such a beautiful pussy in my life.'

Everybody stopped whatever they had been doing, stared at him and roared with laughter. Stephanie, completely unconcerned, went on smoking, and pushed his head towards her crotch. Richard looked at me helplessly, as if imploring me to tell him what to do. I stuck out my tongue and rolled it around my lips, miming my instructions to him. He shook his head, but I ordered him in Dutch, 'Go on! This is your chance to become a real man.'

He grinned at Stephanie, then muff-dived on to her and started eating her with obvious relish . . . at long last! I relinquished my ardent toe-sucker, and rejoined Stephanie on the couch. While Richard continued with his juicy meal, we chatted, as though nothing unusual was taking place. I had already had a glimpse of her fantastic bald pussy, but she now explained that she had recently undergone an operation for appendicitis. Raising her kaftan further, she showed me the band-aid strip, still in place over her scar. Richard glanced up, but he had been taught that good boys do not talk with their mouths full. I let him feed there for ten minutes, and then pulled him away.

'That's enough. Now, go round the room and eat every pussy that you can find.'

It was a miracle. Stephanie's strangely bald pussy had so turned him on that he could not care less what he was going to eat after that. He did as I had ordered him, crawling round the room on his knees, and eating every girl's snatch that came within his reach, apart from those currently occupied by cocks or other tongues. There were eight or so girls, ready, willing and waiting. Some even still had sperm from their previous lovers inside them, but they made him welcome. I wished that I had a camera to catch Richard's expression, as he made his way from one pussy to the next, licking, eating and chewing, at times so violently that the girl would scream with pain, and push him away. He still had not learned tenderness. At last, he reached me.

'Me too,' I told him. 'Now you have to do it.'

His warm tongue darted away eagerly, while he fingered Stephanie's clitoris, which was exposed so invitingly beside me. By now, another girl had crept up behind him and pulled off his black trousers, which he had retained when practically everybody else was naked, apart from a sprinkling of chains, high heels, garter belts and the occasional item of jewellery or a scarf.

The girl, a chubby redhead with monumental tits,

removed the rest of his clothes and began sucking his cock, while he was still fully engaged in eating me and fondling Stephanie. I could see that his cock was ready to explode and I ordered the girl to stop. Richard climbed to his feet, showing off his muscular body, and I shoved him towards Stephanie.

'OK,' I cried. 'Now, fuck her to your heart's content!'

He immediately rammed his great cock into her pussy. She was sufficiently interested to put down her cigarette holder, and a big contented smile spread across her face. Richard was fucking away like a raging bull, holding on to her legs, and I could see that he was approaching his orgasm. As for Stephanie, her features too were contorted by her mounting excitement, and all her guests were watching for their hostess and her partner to explode together.

Suddenly, Stephanie shouted, 'Stop! Get out! I don't want it.'

Richard was shocked, but instead of withdrawing, he kept driving deeper inside her.

Stephanie pushed him away, and then started to laugh. 'It's nothing that you have done. But I dare not have an orgasm; I still have my stitches, and I'm afraid that I'll burst them.'

Everybody saw the funny side of the situation except Richard with his quivering, hard cock. He was disturbed and furious, but I pulled him on to the floor and arranged the tits of the redhead who had sucked him so frantically and then, because of my intervention, had been so shamefully neglected. All he had to do was to position his cock between those mighty mammaries to come and shoot his load over her face and into her hair. She was completely carried away, and had a heavenly look in her eyes as she licked the thick, white sperm from her chin.

For me, this was the fabulous finale of my stay in Paris – the greening of a young lover.

12
Christmas in Spain

I stayed a few days more in Paris before returning with Richard to Amsterdam. I had decided that I would go to Rio de Janeiro for the Carnival in February and March, and that meant a lot of preparations. And Christmas was looming up with its round of parties, and more planning. David, back in Marbella, was grappling with the complexities of Spanish law, so he was condemned to spend the festive season there. It would have been nice to have him with me for the holidays, but he kept me informed of his progress by regular letters and phone calls.

Life had presented him with its usual crop of problems. On arriving back at his apartment, he found that his phone had been cut off because his bank had not paid the bill. In answer to his protests, the bank pointed out that they had never received a bill, which in fact the phone company had sent to Madeleine Carroll's bank. The company informed David that, although he had reported the change of ownership and given details of his bank, it would take them six months to register the details, and as bills were sent every two months, he could expect to be disconnected again soon.

Both Doreen and Marianne were going about their business in Paris, and David found Marbella boring without a girlfriend. So he started seeing more and more of Valerie, a buxom blonde barmaid. She worked in a bar near his apartment, and he would gaze wistfully into her cool grey eyes while he sipped Spanish brandy. She seemed friendly, but David considered it an expensive way of dating a girl. However, persistence eventually paid off. Valerie mentioned a concert on Christmas Eve; David eagerly asked if he could take her, and Valerie agreed. As he told me, either he was alcoholically befuddled or possibly pissed, but he remembered nothing about the forthcoming event, except the date and time. Accordingly, he turned up to pick up Valerie, resplendent in his tightest jeans and a cheerful, jazzy shirt, specially selected for blonde dating. He had borne in mind the reforms of his dressing habits which I had imposed on him. He anticipated that Valerie would be attired in something sexy, and he visualized her in a silver lamé dress which clung seductively to the soft curves of her body. As it was pouring with rain when David called for her, she was swathed in a seaman's foul weather gear, and all that was visible to David was an expanse of mustard-yellow oilskin. He was not sure at which of the discotheques or alternative dives the concert was being held, and was not a little surprised to find himself being ushered into the church for an organ recital.

David was rather self-conscious about the unsuitability of his dress; the church was icily cold and the wooden seats must be the hardest in all Spain. But, since he enjoyed Bach, and was looking forward to enjoying even more the company of Valerie, things could have been worse. His hopes were dashed when, at the end of the recital, she invited him to climb to the organ loft to meet her boyfriend.

'You never told me that you had a boyfriend,' David accused.

'You never asked,' replied the nymph truthfully.

It turned out that Valerie had been going out for many months with a tall, broad-shouldered German who lived in Marbella. He was a fine organist himself, and had helped arrange the series of concerts in the church. Up in the loft, David persuaded the musician who had performed that evening to play the great instrument again. The audience had departed, and the only people present were Valerie, her boyfriend, David, and the organist, Hans Werris, a marvellous artist who, in spite of his being blind, had won a reputation far beyond the boundaries of his native Germany. It was a wonderful experience, perched high above the empty church in the very heart of the massive organ, and they were all so absorbed that they forgot that the organist was a guest of honour at a formal dinner. The other notable guest was no less a personage than the Chancellor of the German Federal Republic who was being kept waiting. There could have been a diplomatic incident, David told me smugly later: wars have been caused by less serious breaches of protocol than starving a visiting head of state.

After his setback, David switched his attentions to a certain Francine, a well-built brunette with lively brown eyes and an attractive dark complexion. Previously he had been deterred from getting better acquainted with her by the presence of a dachshund, which always followed her about and which appeared to have a propensity to bite one's ankles, and by the watery-eyed man who was never far behind the dachshund and who, David feared, might bite more than his ankles. When he discovered that this attendant was Francine's brother, David decided to brave the ferocity of the tiny dog, and his enthusiasm increased when Francine told him that her brother, Yuri, was a fabulous cook.

So David abandoned the bar where the faithless Valerie worked, to patronize a rival establishment where Yuri was cook, manager and general factotum. What finally won him over was when he was served a beautifully prepared steak with a succulent sauce. Maybe the way to a man's heart is through his stomach; that day, David gazed adoringly at Francine with the eyes of a man whose stomach had been seduced. The romance ripened when Francine confided that Yuri's speciality was a bouillabaisse which could put to shame the concoctions which were served up in the South of France, and she promised that she would persuade Yuri to prepare it for him.

Yuri duly announced that, in future, there would be bouillabaisse on Fridays in the bar, which he hoped to be able to convert into a full restaurant. In David's mind, Francine and bouillabaisse became inextricably linked, and he was thinking of the girl as a tasty dish, waiting to be served.

However, the pleasure had to be deferred because, for two successive Fridays, David had business which kept him away from Marbella. The following Friday was one of those days when one catastrophe follows another with sickening regularity, and David was crushed in spirit until he remembered Yuri and the bouillabaisse. The clouds lifted. There are days when a man needs the love of a good woman: there are others when he seeks the solace of good food. David ran to Yuri's bar: his whole future happiness seemed to be enshrined in a casserole.

The bar was strangely empty. Yuri was seated, looking into vacant space. When David greeted him, he remained silent. Impatiently, David demanded bouillabaisse.

'Bouillabaisse is only on Fridays,' Yuri replied moodily.

'But it is Friday,' David pointed out.

'Is it? I forgot. Anyway, I cannot cook when I am upset.'

David remarked that he also was upset and hungry, but to no avail. Yuri had been visited by the police, who had wasted the entire morning with chatter about work per-

118

mits and every other sort of permit which Yuri would need to operate his restaurant. The shattered chef was adamant, he would not prepare a meal until his spirits had been restored. Finally, David took him out to lunch. The meal was expensive, and Yuri never ceased complaining about the quality of the food or the cooking. David realized that life would be hazardous if he were to rely on anyone as temperamental as Yuri, and from then on he began to cook much more at home, but the romance had faded from his relationship with Francine.

David made the fatal error of consulting Alfonso, who stated that out of season, there simply were no chicks about in Marbella, and he had even been forced into the final indignity of becoming faithful to his wife. His advice to David was to visit a bar in Marbella which was patronized by a couple of girls who, for a cash consideration, would be ready, willing and able to oblige him. David was astounded that Alfonso, who had dissipated so much of his time throughout the summer in the vain pursuit of woman-flesh, had neglected to mention the existence of such an establishment.

Alfonso informed him that one of the girls was dark, very attractive and vivacious, with a figure that was full and well-rounded, but not stout. She was a woman of great charm and wit, and reputed to be a fabulous screw. It was inevitable that David found the other one.

Her lair was a bar with the improbable name of Henry IV, but it is doubtful whether Shakespeare would have approved of the dull red paint, the plain wood fittings, stained a dirty brown, the threadbare carpet, or the long, greasy bar. There was a tough-looking barmaid who obviously divined David's needs, and must have been in telepathic communication with Pepita. The young hooker materialized a few minutes after his entry. She boasted

119

the figure of a stunted dwarf running to fat. Her choice of clothes was designed to attract attention; a scarlet mini-skirt revealed a vast expanse of bare thigh. Her face was bland and moon-like, but she had a pretty smile which she directed at her potential customer.

'You buy me a drink,' she explained.

David complied: he needed one himself. Pepita perched on a stool, and demonstrated her sophistication by puffing on a cigarette. She informed David that sleeping with her was the experience of a lifetime and, when he demurred, offered to show him signed references. With a sigh of resignation, he opened negotiations. Pepita was impressed that he had an apartment in the Port, but insisted that he must have a car of a respectable marque. Modestly, David disclosed that he had a Rolls Royce waiting outside.

Pepita was suspicious. 'Is that as good as a Ford?' she enquired.

On receiving his assurance that it was, she graciously condescended to accompany him, although her preference would have been for a Chevrolet rather than the Cor-niche. However, as she climbed into the car, David put the vital question.

'How much?'

'Six thousand pesetas,' Pepita replied unhesitatingly.

David decided that the time had come to explain the facts of life. He pointed out that it was cheaper in Paris, but Pepita was unabashed.

'This is not Paris. It is far more exclusive.'

Firmly David informed her that his need was not that pressing, and he opened the door of the car to let her out. Pepita peeped around, to ensure that nobody could hear her.

'OK,' she whispered. 'Two thousand, but on the condi-ion that when we get back, you say that it was fabulous and that you paid six thousand. If everybody believes that, I can keep up my price.'

In David's apartment, she peeled off her few clothes and climbed on to the bed. She had a worried expression which David's petting did not dispel. It became obvious that she did not know of the existence of foreplay, and when the moment of blissful union arrived, she winced with pain.

'You are so big,' she moaned, 'but it will be all right.'

David narrated to me that he never got into the girl at all, but experienced what can only be described as near intercourse. The young professional was innocent of any technique, and at the end of their encounter, a look of intense relief crossed her face. David apologized if he had hurt her, but Pepita replied that it was merely that it had been so sudden. David was puzzled.

'How many men have you had, Pepita?' he demanded.

'Hundreds! Thousands!' was the airy response.

'Now tell me the truth. How long have you been doing this?'

Unhappily, she admitted to just a few weeks, and agreed that there were some weeks when there had been no customers at all.

'Could it be that I was your first?' David asked.

'Let me count,' she replied unhappily. There was a pause. 'Yes, you were. But you will come back again tomorrow, won't you?'

David promised life-long loyalty, and back at the Henry IV he let everyone know that it had been an unforgettable experience, but fled without going into the gory details.

I was sorry not to be able to minister personally to his affliction, but I was soon to leave for Rio. The best I could do was to send him a bottle of body lotion and instructions on how to use it.

13

Indecent Exposure

As soon as I got to Rio, I looked up some of the people
whose names had been given to me by Pietro, the playboy
of Rome. I was grateful to him, for he introduced me to
some of the most interesting men and women whom I met
during my stay in Brazil. One of them, Luis, and his very
liberal French wife, Vivienne, invited me to stay with
them in their beautiful apartment, overlooking both the
sea and the mountains, in Leblon, a fashionable district
of the city.

Luis was half Indian, and a giant of a man. His house
was littered with primitive Brazilian paintings and statues,
and he had a great collection of records, including classical
as well as hundreds of examples of Brazilian folk music. I
enjoyed listening to the many varied styles; it certainly
was not all loud, carnival sambas, and his music never
failed to put me in a mellow and gay mood.

I spent a lot of time out of doors. Both the tropical
climate and the scenery reminded me of my days in South
Africa and Indonesia. The country was so green, covered
with woods, and all around were lovely hills and mountains. Brazil was one of the most spectacular countries I
have visited, and Rio, a great, sprawling metropolis,
offered everything that one could desire. Endless beaches
of dazzling white sand stretched along the coastline, and
there was a lively city life, with plenty of discotheques,
good restaurants and '*churascerias*', where beef and sausages were served on skewers. I had a marvellous time in

the shops where you could buy those colourful ensembles which the Brazilians love to wear to set off their brown skins. Leather was dirt cheap, and I bought several bags for about a tenth of the price they would have cost back in Europe.

What attracted me more than the shopping and the sightseeing was the friendliness of the people. It was such a refreshing contrast from the frostiness of, for example, the Parisians. Each morning, I would go to the local coffee shop and buy some fresh rolls. The black girl who served me must have been on her feet for twelve hours at a stretch, but she always had a broad smile on her face. In no other country have I encountered this ubiquitous smile, and I asked myself the reason for the eternal 'alegria'. Brazil is a country of great contrasts; there is grinding poverty, but so far I had only come across the happy side of the country.

Then Vivienne had to go away for some weeks, and Luis invited me to accompany him on a trip to Ilheus, and offered to show me some other parts of Brazil. I had not appreciated the vastness of the country, but the drive to Ilheus was several thousand kilometres, and for a city girl like me it was an amazing experience to drive for days along dusty, bumpy roads through the thick forests, in an open jeep.

During the journey, I learned more about Luis. He was thirty-seven and, as well as being a highly respected international lawyer, he and his elder brother, Carlos, owned extensive rubber and cocoa plantations around Ilheus. When we arrived, I remarked on the density of the woods which surrounded us, but Carlos laughed and told me that I should go further north to Manaus, where the Amazon jungle is so rampant that a clearing will be covered once more by vegetation within days. I was staggered to learn that sixty per cent of the planet's oxygen comes from the enormous rain forests of the Amazon.

After a stay of a couple of days, Luis took me on to Bahia, in the state of Salvador, by plane, and this city was the climax of my first fortnight in Brazil. The people were of mixed racial origin: blacks, Indians and Portuguese, without the Nordic strain derived from English, German and Scandinavian immigrants which was evident in Rio and São Paulo; they were also wonderfully good-looking. I would stroll along the beach and admire the voluptuous brown bodies. When they are young, Brazilian women have incredibly firm and sexy buttocks, which are accentuated by their clothes. The tonga, the popular name for a special kind of bikini, leaves practically nothing to the imagination. It consists merely of a string which is pulled through the ass of the wearer, and barely covers the crack of the backside and the pubic area. The men tended to be very macho-looking and often wore full beards, Fidel Castro style.

When Luis had to return to Rio to attend to his business, we checked out of the Meridien Hotel, but I decided to stay on for another week or two in Bahia, and found myself a pleasant small hotel with a swimming pool. It was conveniently close to the beach and the Old Town. There I met an adorable Brazilian journalist named Pablo Porral, whom I called Popo.

He was a bright, sporty young man with many interests, but his main preoccupation was trying to better the lot of his impoverished fellow countrymen, and he showed me the real Bahia, which no official guide would have displayed to a foreigner. In his beaten-up old Volkswagen, we struggled up broken roads and dirt tracks, stopping at shanty towns, and back in the Old Town he took me to cafés and little restaurants, tucked away in secluded corners. There, he would meet his left-wing, intellectual friends, who just about scraped enough of a living to survive.

When I talked with them, I saw the other face of Brazil. In place of *alegria*, there was anger at the plight of the people under the military regime. I suddenly realized how many uniforms I had seen on the streets of Rio and Bahia. On the radio, pop songs were often unsubtle propaganda, extolling the virtues of living in Brazil, designed to keep the population docile and satisfied. But Popo told me of the way people who criticized the government would lose their jobs, or simply disappear. Brazilians who wanted to leave the country were obliged to deposit a thousand dollars, but when they returned, they were repaid in depreciated local currency. There were no cheap charter flights, and Popo himself was saving until he had enough money to get a berth on a freighter and sail to Europe. He was writing a novel, which was based on the conditions in Brazil, and he knew that there was no prospect of it ever being published in his native country.

Popo also took me to see some of the pre-carnival festivities in Bahia, where the Brazilian carnival originated, before it was jazzed up and commercialized in Rio. The *ferias* were fun, everybody singing and dancing in the streets, and the tiny fairs were packed with happy, excited children. The revellers wore brightly-coloured outfits and musicians played lively tunes on every street corner, while black women sat before open fires, serving all kinds of food and candy.

However, it was on the following Saturday that I came into collision with the forces of law and order. I had gone with Popo to the market and bought, among other things, a lovely lace dress, embroidered with white and dark brown flowers, which was virtually see-through. I tried it on, and checked that all the essential parts of my body were sufficiently covered – or so I thought.

After a morning of swimming and walking on the beach, we had worked up quite an appetite, and Popo took me to lunch in a restaurant in a busy shopping mall. As my bikini was still wet, I slipped my new dress over my naked body. The flower design covered my tits, and to be on the safe side, I clutched my beach bag in front of my triangle. What I did not realize was that my un-tanned white ass was peeping through the beige material. I could feel the eyes of dozens of people boring into my back. There were a number of mothers with young kids, but I saw no reason to be uneasy. Popo, on the other hand, was distinctly nervous.

'Don't you have another dress you can wear? You are shocking the upright citizens of Bahia.'

I pointed out that since we were now in the shopping mall, we might as well go straight into the restaurant, and I could not understand the fuss because people must have seen similar dresses before. Still, as soon as we had finished our meal, we beat a hasty retreat. I walked towards the exit on my high heels, my shoulder-length golden hair bobbing up and down. I could scent that there was trouble in the air and I knew that I was being followed. Two security guards were converging on me. I tried to remain calm, and I had almost made it to the door when I felt a hand on my shoulder. My fear was mingled with a wild excitement. I stood motionless, as if nailed to the floor, and had an instant orgasm.

I had become the centre of interest. Around me, a gang of black kids began whistling, and all the women were yelling and laughing at me. Popo's attempt to intervene was futile: we were forced to walk through the streets for twenty minutes to the local police station, where I was hustled into a stinking hot room and locked in. After some time, three respectably-clad police matrons showed up, and started to shout at me, at the top of their voices, that I should be ashamed of myself for not wearing a brassiere and panties beneath my dress. I was sweating, and my naked buttocks were sticking to the broken plastic chair. I protested that I came from Europe, where people would go topless, or even naked, on beaches, and where many women had given up wearing bras. As for my dress, that was Brazilian, and covered me decently. Nevertheless, it took five hours to convince them that I was not a hardened criminal and had committed no offence. I was allowed to leave, after I had promised that in future I would behave myself and, like the good police matrons, I would always wear underwear. Thanks to Popo, I was permitted to depart without paying a fine, but outside I was confronted by dozens of photographers and journalists, and was even requested to appear on a nationally broadcast TV show.

I willingly took up the challenge of the interview, since it gave me an opportunity to denounce the double standards of Brazilian morality. I could be arrested for wearing a flimsy dress, while the police turned a blind eye to the hundreds of parked cars, in which every night couples would be petting or openly screwing. On the average budget, renting an apartment or even a hotel room was an impossibility, hence the use of the cars and motels.

Brazilian motels were quite unlike conventional hotels, and they let the rooms by the hour. The first time I went inside one, I had the impression that I had walked into a cheap whorehouse, with sweet jasmine incense in the air, subdued blue lights and garishly coloured posters on the walls. This was a cheap place, about eight dollars an hour, but on other occasions I was taken to luxurious motels with round beds, push-button phones, six channels of piped music, sexy or romantic, and sometimes even a circular swimming pool outside each room.

A man at the gate hands you a key which gives access to a garage which has a door, rather like a Venetian blind, so that you can look out on to the street, but nobody can see inside and read the number of your car.

I can still remember vividly the shower in one of those fancy motels. At that time I was with a gorgeous mulatto, Joaquim, who had a body like an African wood-carving, lightly tanned and wonderfully muscular. He had the fine features of his German mother and the lovely, thick lips of a Negro. Joaquim, who was a friend of Popo, had taken me to this motel because his wife, like so many Brazilian women, especially those with some black blood in their veins, was intensely jealous at the thought of her husband having an affair with a white woman.

So, there we stood, Joaquim and I, under this superb shower, with the water cascading over our bodies from a spray above my head, another aimed at my ass and a third which played on my pussy. Standing in that tiny space with my body against that glorious hunk of man was marvellously erotic. He too was enjoying the splashing from other jets, and the sight of my body, glistening from the water, excited him to fever pitch. He rubbed the sexy-smelling soap into my flesh with his big hands, and he pushed his dark tinted cock between my buttocks. Leaning forward, he softly bit my back, and my nipples stiffened at once. With our eyes closed, we let our hands feel our streaming wet bodies in a loving embrace. Joaquim took the hand shower and rinsed the soapsuds from me. Then he turned off the water, and once more held me in his arms and stroked my back.

'Close your eyes again,' Joaquim murmured. 'Stand

still and let your body dry. Don't bother to use a towel. Now isn't that a fabulous feeling?'

I had to agree. It was a wonderful, tingling sensation, a unique experience, standing there like two statues. Then he ran his fingers through the wet strands of my hair, and kissed my forehead. His penis reared up, like a space rocket, reaching almost to my breasts. Joaquim took a pink towel, and dried the last traces of water from our bodies. Then he picked me up and carried me to the bed.

From somewhere, he produced a big vibrator with which he massaged my neck, my buttocks, and finally the area around my clitoris, until I was ready to explode. He put the vibrator away, and began to explore my body with his mouth. He sucked on my left nipple with such skill that again I had the sensation that I was about to come, but he knew when to stop to protract my pleasure.

But I could play the same game. I held his magnificent purple cock, with its thick, dark veins, in my mouth, and sucked him until he started to moan, and from his agitated movements I knew that he was within seconds of his orgasm. Abruptly, I stopped and gripped the head of his cock, so that the sperm was forced back. So we played our game of almost come and go until, finally, he brought me to a shattering climax with his thick lips and velvety tongue. At the last moment, Joaquim must have pressed a button, as the mattress began to shudder in a most unusual way, and I came all over his face.

In the background there was insistent samba music, and shortly afterwards Joaquim fucked me to the rhythm. Standing behind the bed, he watched me and himself in the full-length mirror. After licking and sucking my anus, he tried to slip his huge cock into my asshole, but without his realizing it I wriggled my ass to such effect that I was able to manoeuvre him into the front entrance. He was far too big for my near-virgin anus, and my pussy was nice and tight enough to deceive him. With a deep groan, Joaquim thrust his staff inside me and gripped me by the buttocks. As I lifted my head, he bit me really hard on the shoulder, and I came at the same time as him. He was a man who knew how to treat a woman and give her satisfaction.

For several hours we fucked in all sorts of positions, and we finished with a session on the air mattress in the pool. It was fun, but it needed a fair amount of acrobatic skill, and there were comical moments when we fell off the lilo and climbed back on again.

At the end of our hot afternoon Joaquim pushed a button, and a few minutes later a butler in a pink suit arrived, carrying a tray on which there was chocolate milk, hot coffee and, discreetly folded in a silver casket, the bill, based on the time we occupied the room. There were also a couple of candies in multicoloured wrappers bearing the name of the hotel. Joaquim told me that many unfaithful husbands had been discovered by their vengeful wives, simply because they had left the tell-tale candies in their pockets.

So, when I was before the TV cameras, I talked freely of the sham morality of Brazil. If I had tried to do the same thing in Argentina at that time, Popo assured me, I would have joined the ranks of the 'disaparecidos', those who had disappeared mysteriously and were never seen again. But he agreed with what I said about the Brazilians' double standards. There was plenty of sexual activity, but it was taboo to talk about it, and books and films were heavily censored.

Still, there could be a more light-hearted treatment of the Brazilian male and his amours. In a film whose title was translated as *Flor and her two husbands* which was based on a book by Jorge Amado, a famous writer who lived in Bahia, the heroine becomes a widow when her first husband, a regular Don Juan, suffers a fatal heart attack, surrounded by girls. She remarries a boring, middle-aged pharmacist, but her first mate's ghost returns to haunt her. Although he had made her suffer during his lifetime, he is still able to get her into all sorts of trouble now that he is dead. Such is the Brazilian macho; even his death does not put an end to his womanizing exploits, nor does it bring any relief to his widow.

The time came for me to quit Bahia. The last few days were marred by the insistence in some of the small hotels that a man and a woman could not share the same room unless they were respectably married. Once or twice, I was able to smuggle Popo into my room, but eventually we simply registered as Mr and Mrs Porral. And this was in carnival season! So much for Brazilian morality.

14
Carnal Carnival

Back in Rio, I bumped into a couple of girls who had worked for me in New York – two ex-happy hookers. They had bought and furnished two apartments which they rented out, so they did not need to go back to their old trade, at least for a while. But can a leopard change its spots? Once a hooker, always a hooker.

I had met some wealthy men, and had been invited to go to the Carnival ball. I introduced Andrea and Eugenia to two men who were looking for partners and who bought them tickets for the ball at $150 per seat. I was with the men, preparing to go and pick up the girls, when they called me to ask whether they were going to be paid for the evening.

'What the hell!' I exploded. 'You get free tickets for the ball, you can eat to your heart's content, dance the whole evening and probably fuck any nice young man you see. You will be able to make some great connections, and you are not even obliged to have sex with these friends of mine. Just this once, consider yourselves off duty. This is carnival: have fun, forget business.'

How happy I felt that the Happy Hooker period of my life was over and done with.

That evening, the six of us went to the Canecao ball, an unbelievably colourful affair. The proceedings started with the '*desfile de fantasia*', a parade of men and women, showing off their costumes and fantastic headdresses, and generally enjoying themselves. Thousands of people took part, and there were prizes awarded for the best costume, for the most imaginative creation perched on their heads (you could not call them hats) and for many other categories. A costume could cost as much as $1,500, and some were studded with genuine amethysts. Impoverished working families would go hopelessly into debt in order to have a sufficiently splendid carnival costume. The band struck up 'Ciudade Maravillosa' and the entire *desfile* moved off. The carnival had started.

The ball took place in three enormous interconnecting halls in one of Rio's best hotels. Each room had its own live band, playing until five in the morning. There were women of all ages, with glittering eye make-up, shiny costumes and flowers in their hair, escorted by some very handsome men. They danced and sang without pause. Our table was well placed to watch the moving sea of bodies, but it was impossible to keep up a conversation through the deafening samba music. All around us, people were wearing masks, more fantastic than anything that I could ever have dreamed of.

Once the meal was finished, we three girls decided that we were not going to sit at the table with our rather formal companions. They had invited us to come to a ball, and since they were neither lovers nor clients, why not have a ball? That is how I came across Franz, a good-looking, twenty-year-old Hungarian. He was utterly charming, with the perfect manners of an old aristocratic family, and Andrea immediately tried to take him away from me, but without success. Franz and I became insep arable, but Andrea soon gained a consolation prize in a handsome, nineteen-year-old German, while Eugenia was fully occupied with an elderly rich Italian, who had his eye on her early in the evening. So, we were all contented. For the sake of appearances, we would occasionally return to our table, sip a drink and look attentive and serious.

133

Then we would jump to our feet, scamper into one of the other halls and dance our feet off with the men we had chosen for the evening.

Of course, the ball was only the beginning. In Franz, I found a tender and emotional friend. I learned that his father had left Hungary and settled in Rio twenty years ago, before Franz was born, and that his mother was now living in the north with a well-to-do cattle breeder, and working in the local Lufthansa office. Franz himself delighted in wearing French or Italian designer clothes and fancy scarves, which suited him well. At first I thought that he was gay, but later, when I got to know him better, I found that his sexuality was of a completely different character.

Like Popo, Franz took me to several motels, but whereas Popo was an accomplished lover who never failed, Franz only managed to make love to me in a normal manner a few times, and even then I had to assist him with a great deal of manual stimulation. While he was penetrating me, I would hold his penis very tight between my fingers, and he would kneel above me. He was a bit too skinny for my taste, but such a nice, sympathetic person that I could not resist his entreaties to let him take me to various motels. However, their brothel-like atmosphere began to get on my nerves, and what was more, Franz's problem in getting it up was giving me an inferiority complex. He did not want to talk about it, and at first refused to answer my questions, but I persisted, and eventually learned the truth about him.

Before he felt sufficiently relaxed to confide in me, Franz took me away for a week to Buzios, a place I had heard called the St Tropez of Brazil. After a four-hour drive, we arrived and found Buzios a much rougher and less sophisticated resort than any on the French Riviera.

We were plagued by mosquitos, but fortunately our hotel had screens on the windows, so our sleep was undisturbed.

On our first night, Franz suggested that we take a walk on the beach, and go skinny-dipping under the full moon. We had a wonderful time in the sea and our bodies glistening from the water we gazed up at the thousands of stars and the glorious silver moon. It was the ideal setting for romance. After all, how many more whorehouse bedrooms in the motels could we face? We were all alone, apart from the distant barking of a dog. I lay on my back on the sand, and Franz leaned over me. As he kissed and caressed me, his penis began to grow erect. One thing that he could do well was kiss. His mouth was not very big, but his tongue was an adventurous explorer of all the parts of my body which were waiting to be discovered. I held him gently and rubbed my finger underneath his scrotum. To my delight, his penis grew harder. He could never produce an instant hard-on, and often was unable to reach orgasm inside me, so that I would have to finish him by hand. But this was one of those perfect evenings when nothing could go wrong.

He had just entered me when we were joined by the dog. It appeared from nowhere, running around us, and barking furiously. Franz watched the circling hound, and then noticed that there were half a dozen crabs scuttling up the beach towards us. They were such big, ugly creatures that I screamed when I caught sight of them. In seconds, our romantic night had been transformed into a hilarious farce. Franz leaped to his feet, as though he had been stung by a thousand bees. We had not brought towels with us, and we raced along the beach without stopping until we were safely back in our hotel room.

By degrees, Franz explained his problem. It was not

simply that he was a masturbator. That was something which I would have understood and with which I would have been able to cope. He had a strict Catholic family background, and his mother and his sisters had been a frustrating influence on him: he was even forbidden to bring girls home. But one night, when his mother was away visiting his father, he smuggled me into the house. Lying in bed he told me his story.

'About four o'clock one afternoon, I was standing in front of the window looking at the apartment opposite. A girl of about fourteen was seated, reading a book. She wore glasses and appeared to be doing her homework. I had on a pair of light beige flannel trousers which were rather tight-fitting and a shirt with a belt. Suddenly, I developed an immense hard-on, something which is so difficult for me when I am close to a girl. I began to walk to and fro, hoping to attract her attention, and after a few minutes she looked up and smiled. I stood still and began to rub my penis through my trousers. She looked amazed, but went back to her reading. My penis was really throbbing, and I decided to draw the Venetian blinds in such a way that she would be able to see only the bottom half of my body. However, first I slowly undid each button of my shirt and removed the cuff-links, before taking it off. The girl pretended to go on reading, but she kept glancing up at me. She crossed her legs and smiled again.

'I fantasized on how her tiny pussy, probably still hairless, was getting juicy and soaking her white cotton underpants. Perhaps her nipples were standing erect. These thoughts excited me and my penis was absolutely rigid. She was able to see only my belt and the top of my trousers. She probably did not realize that I could watch her and see every move she made. I had made up my mind that I had to exhibit myself to this little girl. I found the thought that I might get caught exhilarating. She still held her book, but I could see her peeping at the window.

'I unzipped my trousers and pulled out my cock. Immediately, her mouth gaped open, and I started to masturbate. Then I noticed an older woman, her mother I suppose, standing close to her chair. I did not want to get caught, so I turned away. The girl was blushing and she picked up the book which she had let drop. I had a pair of binoculars handy and I watched her until the woman left. Then I went back to my masturbating, while the girl watched me openly. As I felt my orgasm approach, I jerked up the Venetian blind, stared at her full in the face, and my come spat on to the window. She jumped up with a scream, and ran away.'

Franz told me that he had had several similar experiences.

'You have seen our mulatto maid,' quite sexy but nothing exceptional,' he resumed. 'Some nights I come home late when everybody is asleep, and I go into her room and look at her, lying there on her side, with a sheet covering the top part of her body. Her bare legs stick out, and sometimes I can see her ass as well. I crouch behind her and wait until I am sure that she is fast asleep. Then I open up my trousers, and masturbate as close to her as I can get, with my cock practically rubbing against her legs.'

There were times when the maid would be watching television, and Franz would creep up behind her and masturbate, catching his sperm in a tissue, while the girl was completely unaware of what was going on. I felt flattered that Franz had confided in me, and from that time on we were completely at ease with each other. Franz was more relaxed, and as he enjoyed being with me, his sex life improved markedly as well.

Back in Rio, Franz took me to a lot of places which I would never otherwise have seen, for instance the tiny Teatro Opinao. There was practically no ventilation, and as the place was packed, the heat was stifling and the sweat was running off me. But on stage there was a sort of Brazilian jam session, with one group of musicians following another. The rhythm was overpowering, and under the spell of the music I forgot all about my discomfort. Some of the songs had political themes, but most were sad and sentimental. Many of the country's best-known writers and composers, such as Jorge Amado, Carlos Joabim, Chico Barque and Vinicius de Morais had made the theatre famous. I found the coming and going of the sweat-soaked bodies in the confined space strangely sensual. That night there was a famous lesbian singer, Maria Bethania, in the audience, surrounded by her usual dozen groupies. She needed little urging to oblige with a terrific song; it was the highlight of the evening.

Another night we went to the so-called 'Transvestite Ball' in a dilapidated cinema in the old part of the town, which had been specially done up for the occasion. The seats had been removed so that there was a big dance floor. For the first time in my life, I got really scared in a crowd. The freaky character of the ball had attracted a vast number of people, and the heat was getting to everybody. Thousands of spectators were trying to squeeze through the entrance which was barred by a cord; only those who had bought their tickets in advance were being let in. To try to fight one's way through the shouting, jostling crowd was a terrifying experience. I clutched Franz's hand, but after a few seconds I was swept away from him. It took me half an hour to struggle into the hall, and in the process I lost a handbag and one shoe. But I managed to keep hold of the ticket which, at last, got me into the ball. In the middle of the frenzied mob I could glimpse some of the drag-queens, their make-up dripping off their faces, false eyelashes falling, and wigs knocked to the ground. It was a pathetic spectacle.

The mounting hysteria led to tragedy. I was nearly killed when I was pushed against a wall and could not move, while the crowd continued to shove and pull until I began to grow numb and lose all sensation. Miraculously, I slithered out of this sauna and reached the cord. But I saw a woman virtually decapitated within a few feet of me. She was bending down to get under the cord when a man behind her pushed forward, crushing her head against the rope. I heard a half scream, followed by low gurgling sounds amid the yelling and cheering all around. The woman collapsed on to the floor, where I suppose she was trampled to death. It was a horrifying sight, but there was nothing that anybody could do, and nobody even seemed to care. Next day, I learned from the newspapers that fifty-three people had been crushed to death that night in the Carnival crowds.

Inside the hall it was even hotter, but at least there was space to walk and to dance. Bright spotlights played on the dancers, picking out fantastic costumes and hair-dos, and heightening the surrealist impression of the vivid colours and strange forms of the decor. Some of the transvestites were truly beautiful and were a match for any woman. Many had undergone plastic surgery, and not only tits had been fixed, but noses, chins and asses. One of the drags told me proudly that Rio was Gay Power City Number One, at least during Carnival.

There were impersonations of Judy Garland, Barbra Streisand and Liza Minelli by well-known transvestite performers. During one of these intermissions, I over-heard a couple of macho males who could not believe that such lovely creatures were really men. In fact, I knew that transsexuals were not allowed to participate. What these lascivious spectators did not realize was that they would not have tolerated such exaggerated behaviour from real women, whom they would have condemned as wild man-eaters.

Franz summed it up. 'A transvestite is somebody who would like to be a woman, and so acts in a super-feminine manner. She needs to shock or to charm, and so all those little moves and gestures are overdone. The camp is meant to give that extra bit of spice.'

After that ball, I thought that I knew all there was to know about crowds, but I was wrong. The president of a cosmetics company invited me to go with him to the Avenido Rio Branco, to watch the most famous of all the parades, the *desfile de escuelos de samba*. He distrusted Brazilian banks, and kept all his cash as well as his credit cards in his jacket pocket, and that night he was also holding my leather handbag with my camera inside, as well as some food, for the parade would go on for many hours. We did not bother to turn up until after midnight, since that was when the best of the samba schools were due to pass. This turned out to be a mistake, for the crowds were so dense that it was impossible for us to fight our way through to occupy our expensive reserved seats. Far more tickets had been sold than there were seats, and the scene was chaotic; the flimsy stands were overcrowded and whole sections of them collapsed, while boys selling Coca Cola and ice creams snaked their way through the mob, holding their trays high above their heads.

We were standing on a stairway, underneath the balustrade, trying to catch a glimpse of the parade, when I saw some spectators in the stand pissing between the seats right on to a woman below, who was shouting and protesting, but was jammed too tight to get out of the way. Of course, the people in the stands had no way of leaving their places to attend to a call of nature. We decided that we had suffered enough, and that we would watch the rest of the show on TV. There was the same scrimmage to get out; but at last we were free and were making our way along a dark alley at the end of which the car was parked.

From nowhere, a middle-aged black man rushed towards us, dived into my companion's pocket with one hand and seized my bag with the other. In less than a second, he had ripped away the pocket and made off with all the man's cash and valuables. I screamed and managed to grab hold of my handbag and hang on for grim death. We had had enough of the great Rio Carnival! The streets were teeming with hit and run thieves and pickpockets, and people on the beaches made a practice of carrying nothing other than a packet of cigarettes and a lighter, securely fastened round their necks by a chain.

By the time I left the country I had got to know quite a number of Brazilians. The men, like European Latins, tended to be macho and, among the better families, extremely conservative. Proud and handsome, the Brazilian male is the perfect gentleman, until he gets to the bedroom. There, the girl must submit to whatever treatment is meted out to her, no matter how rough, and never complain. She is expected to moan and groan to turn him on, and anal intercourse is very much in vogue. As for the female of the species, by the time she is twenty-five, the working-class woman will have lost whatever figure she had. The richer women spend a fortune on plastic surgery, and their vanity is boundless. Wives would look bored while their husbands stood about, chatting about business

141

or some trivialities with each other, or openly flirting with very young girls. But when they were over forty, often boredom would turn to real bitterness, and their marriages became mere formalities. Yet these women were in many cases insanely jealous, and husbands who travelled abroad and discovered a broader perspective would frequently acquire a new wife from the United States or Europe. My host, Luis, had been married four times, and always outside Brazil.

The most beautiful women in Brazil were the mulattos. I met a gorgeous girl called Manuella; she was only sixteen, but was the most sensuous creature I have ever seen. Her soft body was voluptuous; full tits with purple nipples, dark skin, and hair raven black and as curly as a lion's mane. She had the face of a fallen angel, always smiling, and her even white teeth made a pleasing contrast with her brown skin. She had delicate hands and the fingers of an artist, so I was not surprised to learn that she wanted to become a painter, and she had already done a few quite good paintings as well as some sculpture.

I had met Manuella one night when Luis and Vivienne had invited me to dinner along with three Brazilian friends. All three men were desperately trying to make a pass at her, but I complimented her on her hair and her hands in my own manner. She was sitting across the table from me, and I gently took her hand in mine and caressed her fingers. The men had been clumsily pushy, and made their intentions all too obvious. She had heard of my reputation, and did not know quite what to make of me, but she was intrigued, since she had never made love to a woman, and Luis allowed me to take her back to his house and spend the night with her.

My Manuella not only looked like a lion: in bed she proved to be a tigress and was not to be tamed. She insisted that she had never bedded another woman, but she was a most eager pupil. Holding a glowing candle close to my clitoris, I was able to point out to her the erogenous zones, and in no time she had learned how to do what, and where to do it. Within half an hour, she had sucked me to an orgasm.

However, first she kissed my body with her full, purple lips. Her tongue darted wildly inside my mouth, playfully sucking my tongue. Touching each other was a great sensation, for our bodies were so different. Manuella was short and inclined to be stocky, but with phenomenal buttocks, strong thighs, enormous, firm breasts, and a skin as soft as a peach. When she suggested that we suck our own tits, we both burst out laughing. Manuella made a hell of a lot of noise: she could be clearly heard in the next block, and she soon aroused the attention of Luis and Vivienne.

I cannot stand rough treatment of my tits or my clit, but Manuella begged me to give her nipples a succession of short, quite hard bites, and when I sucked her terrific breasts she practically went through the ceiling. By now I had placed my mattress on the floor, so that our playground extended over the whole room, and we certainly needed all the space. Manuella was extremely strong, and she gripped me tight. We rolled all over the floor, like a couple of wild cats, and I found myself in every corner of the room, without once letting go of that luscious body. Glancing up, I saw that we had been joined by our host and hostess, who stood hugging and kissing each other before retiring to a couch, obviously inspired by our antics. I gazed at Vivienne's boyish figure, with its almost invisible tits, and Luis's massive, square body from which his cock stood out like a gigantic totem pole.

But Manuella demanded all my attention. She had turned her body at such an angle that she was able to flick her tongue back and forth between my ass and my pussy, while I was playing with her clit. But now I noticed her feet, as dainty and graceful as her hands, and I knew that I had to suck her toes, one by one. This sent the sweet girl into total ecstasy, and I revelled in her strong, horny odour. I was intent on devouring this wild animal, since I knew that it might be a long time before I would come across anyone as hot and passionate again. She had a large clitoris, but just before she exploded in my mouth, it was so swollen that it felt like a miniature penis. No sooner had she come than I climbed over her and mounted her like a man. Pushing my knee between her thighs, I fucked her, while I pressed my own pussy against her leg, so that our throbbing cunts soared to another orgasm.

Our bodies were soaked with perspiration, and both of us must have lost quite a bit of weight that night. In the morning, I found that my back was covered with scratches where my wild woman had clawed me. But when we tried to get some sleep, my tigress became a little kitten, snuggling up to me and demanding affection. She lay with her thick black curls cupped against my armpits, and her big, brown eyes staring up at me. I suspected that the girl was falling in love.

I was awakened at about eight by a draught which set me sneezing, and my plight had Manuella in fits of laughter. She was wide awake, but I felt like a washed-out midnight cowboy, and I simply had to get some rest, as I had a very full day planned. So I called her a taxi, and sent her home. She got up and dressed reluctantly, and when I walked her to the taxi she burst into tears, complaining that I had sent her away.

For me, that tumultuous night had been wonderful fun, a great romp in the hay, but I could not become truly emotionally involved with her. Intellectually, we had little in common, and her English was so faltering that a serious conversation would have been impossible. But I liked her a lot and she was the epitome of the sex-kitten.

However, I had not seen the last of Manuella. It was a week or two later, during one of the Carnival parades, when I was accompanied by Franz, that I met this charming creature again, and we celebrated that afternoon with a fabulous *partie à trois*. It gave Franz the opportunity for his ultimate fantasy, for although Brazilians claim not to be racists, the richer families disapprove of their children having friends who are not pure white. So, for Franz, this beautiful mulatto was forbidden fruit and, as he proved, passion fruit. Here was full scope for his exhibitionism, and not only could he masturbate before her, but actually fuck her as well.

A few days later, my Brazilian rhapsody drew to a close, and I boarded the plane to take me back to Europe. That last session with Manuella and Franz had provided a worthy finale.

15

Some of My Best Friends are Jewish . . .

Despite all my adventures and the excitement of colourful Brazil, I began to have pangs of homesickness. It was good to be back in Europe, to drive to Paris, where I visited friends and breathed in culture, and in Amsterdam, June brought the Holland Festival, the Festival of Fools, and all the latest movies which I had missed in Brazil. It also brought my birthday, 15 June, and soon afterwards I decided that the time had come for me to return to Marbella. I did not look forward to doing the long drive alone, so I invited an old friend, George Silversmith, who lived in London, to accompany me. As we were in no hurry, we thought it would be fun to make a detour, stopping for a few days in Paris and then going on to St Tropez, where we booked into the charming Hotel le Monche for a couple of weeks.

I had known George since I was a child, and I found that more and more I was bumping into people who had been at school with me. Such meetings tended to be nostalgic: we always had our memories of youth and innocence in common. But the course of our later lives had diverged: some friends were married and settled, others had broken loose from marital ties, some had risen high on the social ladder, made big money and adopted very right-wing, capitalist views, while others were barely making a living, or were even unemployed, and were usually on the left of the political spectrum.

I had not seen much of George when we were at school. I remembered him as a rather plump, lonely boy with a

146

drooping jaw, a prominent Jewish nose and heavy eyelids, and with a tendency to squint as if he were solving some difficult problem. His clothes were shabby and his general appearance that of a rather shady character: nobody really trusted George. He would often skip classes and was what we would call in Dutch '*een slordig type*', an easy-going fellow, not burdened with too many scruples. He always had something to sell, either to his fellow pupils or to the staff, but his most lucrative line was wholesaling rubbers to boys in the highest classes. When a girl got pregnant and accused him of having pricked a hole in the condom, George's rejoinder was that she ought not to have attempted to economize by using it over and over again. His parents were poor and skimped and saved to be able to send their son to one of Amsterdam's best schools, but George left after four years and I heard nothing more of him until shortly after my return from Canada.

For a whole year, I was being urged to meet him by friends who told me that he was greatly changed, an honest, prosperous, hard-working businessman, married and with two adorable daughters. Although he now lived in London, he made frequent business trips to Holland, and he called me a few times and proposed that we go out together. I was not too anxious, since I was fully occupied with dating unmarried guys.

Then, one day, he phoned and told me that he had broken with his wife. He sounded very depressed and so, after six months of sporadic telephone conversations, we met again. I could not believe my eyes. The sloppy, round-shouldered nebbish had grown into a handsome, polite, sporty, muscular young man. He was well dressed and groomed, and informed me that he was the proud owner of an international telecommunications systems bureau.

It was clear to me that he needed somebody to love and take care of him, but as he was living in England and I was moving around a great deal, I was not prepared to enter into the sort of steady relationship which he would have liked. I was enjoying my freedom, although I was willing to give him my heart when we were together. George welcomed the opportunity of our holiday. He was being driven crazy by lawyers who were raising every conceivable problem over his divorce, refusing to sign papers and not allowing him to see his children. He was drinking heavily, and he had been obliged to surrender his driving licence, so he was dependent on others to chauffeur him. His closest friend was a Dutch lawyer called Mark who, as it happened, was also in the throes of a divorce, and felt that he could do with a break. I knew and quite liked Mark, so when he asked if he could join us in Marbella, I raised no objection.

Meanwhile, George's drinking was causing a sexual problem. I told him straight that I could not tolerate a man whose impotence was the result of alcoholism, and I insisted that he went on the wagon. Such was the love for me which he had developed that he gave up booze at once, and there was a gratifying improvement in his sexual prowess. Poor George did undergo ghastly withdrawal symptoms for weeks, feeling as if he were suffering frightful hangovers, although he was completely sober. Things got so bad that his doctor told him to take a glass of wine with his meals: the break had been too abrupt.

In bed at first I was altogether too aggressive for him, but the moments when he loved me most and fucked me best were when I was very tired and already half asleep. It made me think of necrophilia and at times I would pretend to be sleeping, for the more passive I was, the more active George became. I grew to understand that, for George, sex was something precious, to be handled with silk gloves, and there was no way that I could tell him what to do. He was not a man to fuck on command, and an impromptu quickie was definitely out of the question. But he was good for me, teaching me to relax and be patient, and not always seize the initiative. Eventually we got it together: our orgasms would be simultaneous, and George showed himself to be one of the most gentle, romantic lovers of my life. He had a beautiful body which fitted perfectly with my own, and he would spend hours stroking my neck, my arms or my hands, and kissing my earlobes in the movies or when I was driving. But his strongest fixation was my tits which he could suck for ever, even falling asleep like a baby suckling at its mother's breast.

But George would periodically disappear, and I began to have some suspicions, which were confirmed when I discovered that he had another, secret life. George would pick up whores on the street or in the windows of canal houses. His choice was vulgar, heavily made-up women with gigantic tits, and with these aggressive types he had no difficulty in getting a hard-on. I knew that his wife, like his mother, was a rather dowdy, conventional person, and I suppose that he loved me as a woman whose character lay satisfactorily between these two extremes. Anyway, I did not mind his sorties. Now that he had stopped his heavy drinking he was capable of coming more than once a day, and he had plenty of energy for me, as well as for his 'other' life-style.

There are times when I feel that I must be something of a racist. Looking back at the men in my life whom I have truly loved and with whom I have had a long-lasting relationship, it seems that all of them were Jewish. There was first my father, of whom I still have incestuous dreams. My ex-fiancé, Carl, was Jewish, but would never admit it. Very different was Larry, the Silver Fox, a typical New York Jew. Then I fell in love with Paul, the man who most resembled my father, who became my husband for several years, and whom I have loved more than anybody else. Now there was George, and in a totally different way, David, who was more of a buddy and also something of a father figure. I also realized that all these men, especially David, were complex characters, and that I am attracted to people who are not simple and absolutely happy, but who look at me more for psychological support than merely physical relief.

Mark was flying directly to Marbella, so when I drove to St Tropez only George was with me, feeding me and keeping me awake with witty chat, for I was behind the wheel for ten or twelve hours a day. When we arrived I looked up Leo, whom I had known in New York, where he had been a swinger, and kept an open house which was always full of people who loved to fuck, but who usually overstayed their welcome.

Now he only accepted guests who had been formally invited, but his house at St Tropez, where he lived like a hermit composing music, was restrained and lonely after his menage in New York. Like me, Leo had done his share of travelling. Were we searching for happiness, or simply running away from ourselves? Sexually, Leo had become utterly blasé. He had done everything, read all the porno books, seen all the kinky films and participated in, or organized, every kind of orgy.

'I might get excited,' he admitted with a wry grin, 'if I got a phone call in the middle of the night, inviting me to come and watch a nun being fucked by two horses, but I would prefer something rather more way out.'

I recalled seeing a movie, back in his old home, where

a Danish chick did it with every species of animal – donkeys, dogs, and even a pig with a corkscrew cock. I believed him when he said that conventional sex no longer turned him on. Now he had become serious, even philosophical.

'Xaviera, do you know how I can tell that I am getting old? When you are young, you count the days when you feel bad, but when you are old, you count those when you feel good. There have not been many of those lately,' he added sadly.

I think that Leo, whose wife had just left him, was one of the loneliest men I have known. But I was sure that within a couple of months he would have found himself a young blonde and be happily and busily back at work, probably in California where he was well-known.

Leo proposed that we stay with him for a few days, and we were glad to move in. He could not understand that George was no swinger, but strictly a one-woman guy. One afternoon, George and I were in our room, getting ready for some pre-siesta sex, when Leo strode in, carrying a tray loaded with cold chicken, olives, cheese, gherkins and even a few mint leaves. All he was wearing was a cock-ring around his balls and the base of his penis. He was in excellent shape; I cannot remember him ever having difficulty in getting a hard-on. In view of his hospitality, I could not turn him away when he joined us on the king-size bed, and started to caress my body with a bottle of Nivea Milk which he produced. As he rubbed the lotion into my soft skin, Leo's cock grew, but George's began to shrink. George could have learned a lot about making love from Leo and so, although I knew that I was hurting George, I began to concentrate on my host's advances, and soon his body was as glistening with the body milk as my own.

Standing behind the bed, Leo pulled my legs over his shoulders, and penetrated me with strong thrusts. We made strange, squishy sounds, and the afternoon sun bathed our bodies in a golden glow. He could hold out for a long time without coming, and I had three orgasms, with him going down on me and fucking me in ten different positions.

It was then that I noticed in the hallway a church stool which Leo had bought for decoration and hanging on the wall was a bishop's robe, a sumptuous purple affair with lots of gold thread. I got this kinky notion that I wanted to get fucked in church, while the priest was celebrating mass. So I begged Leo to put on the robe and fuck me, as I knelt on the low wooden bench. I folded my hands, as if in prayer, while, with the gorgeous robe hoisted high above his buttocks, Leo acted out my fantasy until, with a loud moan, he reached his climax, and I almost squeezed his balls into my cunt.

I climbed to my feet with Leo's sperm running down my legs, and only then realized that George had been present through all our performance. He was lying on his stomach with a pillow pulled over his head, so as not to see or hear our love-making. I have a special place in my heart for Leo and I could not resist the urge to make love with him, but I was pleased that George was jealous and a bit of an old-fashioned square. He would never be like David, who was always happy if I were happy, even with somebody else, but then, I did not love David as much as I loved George.

We met a much more contented man, living on a luxurious yacht in the bay with a pretty French girl. His name was Arthur James, and he had written a lot of books on the so-called primal scream therapy, which he had invented. George was crazy about sailing and intersted in psychology, so we spent some days on their boat, sailing from one coastal village to the next. They were not swingers, and we were perfectly relaxed, lying nude in the sunshine, as the yacht nosed its way through the clear water.

In Nice we picked up Herb, whom I had known in Toronto and invited to Marbella. He was a Persian Jewish lawyer, tall, dark and good-looking with fine, brown eyes, long curling eyelashes and a bush of crinkly black hair, both on his head and on his chest. Herb was twenty-nine and bright, but very immature in his behaviour towards women. He looked the perfect playboy, but living on his own and without any sort of responsibility, despite his high income, he was extraordinarily stingy. He stayed with me for three weeks, and never even offered to buy me a drink. Since he was only my guest, and not my lover, I was not too concerned.

Herb had a weakness for blondes, so one day on the beach I introduced him to Ingrid, a Swedish girl with lovely shoulder-length golden hair cut in the same style as mine, a sweet face and sparkling eyes as blue as the waters of a mountain lake. She had charm and beauty, and if her intelligence left something to be desired, Herb's slogan was 'Who cares about brains with a body like that?' George and I watched the blossoming of their romance. I did not spoil things for Herb by telling him that I remembered Ingrid from the year before, as a footloose drifter who wandered from one bed to another, and who would stay with any man who would give her a bite to eat and some booze. She was not a demanding girl, but did get thirsty. So the afternoons passed with her lying on one mattress on the beach getting drunk, while Herb lay on another, ogling her. During the day, other men would supply Ingrid with drinks: at night, Herb supplied her with his cock.

George and I would go out for dinner, but Herb and Ingrid never joined us, and when we got home, they were either fucking or sleeping. On the third day, I asked Herb where they had eaten.

'We haven't bothered to go out for meals,' he replied. 'We just live on love.'

In fact, Herb would raid my fridge in the morning, and store up enough energy to fuck Ingrid while saving himself the cost of a meal. But, after the third night, Ingrid disappeared. She had had enough – or too little, which in this case was the same thing. Herb was heartbroken. He refused to go with us to other beaches or up into the mountains, and hung about the same spot where he had first met Ingrid, hoping that she would return. He borrowed my motorbike and scoured the bars, enquiring after her, but nobody would admit to having seen her. Herb, waiting on the beach, went crazy, but he did get a lovely suntan.

Weeks later, I came across Ingrid in Randy's, a pub in the Old Town, where she was working as a barmaid.

'He was too serious,' she told me. 'Instead of getting me something to eat or drink, he kept telling me that I was just the sort of girl that he had always wanted to marry, and offering to buy me a ticket to go back with him to Canada. Mind you, there was a condition. Once I was there, I was to get a job and repay him the fare. He was super-horny and not a bad lover, but who can live on air?' She laughed and poured a drink for a customer. 'Boy, was he sticky! He couldn't keep his hands off me. But that is enough. No more Persians for me, please!'

'Except on the floor, perhaps?' I suggested.

From the look she gave me, I knew that Ingrid had not the faintest idea what I meant.

16

Trips to the Mountains

was pleased to see David again and find out how he was making out. He was cheerful and in good health, but did not seem to be getting much action. Still, he did appear to be making up in cultural activity for what was lacking in his sex life. After his unexpected excursion with Valerie, he had gone to more organ concerts in the church, and he invited me to accompany him to a rather unusual one in which two young French girls would play – four hands and four feet on one organ, along with a trumpeter.

could not help imagining what might be going on in the organ loft, and just how intertwined their limbs might be at the end of the recital, so I agreed to go, and I brought George with me.

We had no difficulty in finding seats, and soon we were chatting with the two couples who were on either side of us. On my left were Rudi and Valya, Rumanian Jews now living in Colombia, while on our other side sat Bob and Sharon, also Jews, although Bob was of Hungarian descent.

'You have to go to a church to find Jews,' David commented acidly and, turning to Bob, 'What's a nice Yiddisher boy like you doing in a place like this?'

Although all of them claimed to be music lovers, the programme was long and the seats were hard, and soon there were signs of restlessness on my left. The music ranged from early Baroque to ultra-modern. Somehow, the girls managed to find yet more pieces to play as encores, and as the church grew colder and the hardness

155

of the pews more oppressive, faint groans arose from the Rumanian camp. Eventually, we emerged from the church with gladdened hearts but frozen limbs, and very, very sore bottoms.

Over cups of hot coffee in the Port, we agreed to meet the following day. Our new acquaintances were anxious to get to know me better, so I proposed that we take a trip together to one of the tiny picturesque towns which perch on the mountains overlooking the coast in this part of Spain. David surprised me by saying that he would be busy and not able to make the trip.

'Since when have you had no time for me, and who is she?' I demanded.

David assumed an air of injured innocence. 'I have promised an outing to Alfonso, with whom I have often enjoyed the hunt, but somehow never been in at the kill. As always, nothing will happen, but the experience should be good for a laugh.'

As George had arranged to play tennis with Mark, it was just the five of us who set out the following morning for Casares, and we fitted comfortably in my BMW, or so I thought, from the driving seat. But after a few kilometres there was a complaint from the back seat that the car was swaying violently from side to side. As the road consisted of a succession of tight hairpin bends, out of consideration for their stomachs I slowed down: it was lucky that I did.

I swung round one particularly vicious bend, and narrowly missed colliding with the crumpled wreck of what had once been a Volkswagen. The driver must have gone into the bend too fast, straight into the path of an oncoming truck. Glass and twisted metal covered the road, which was completely blocked. Close by stood a

olice van and some traffic cops, their motorbikes flanking
n ambulance into which, at that very moment, the badly
ijured occupants of thc smashed car were being carried.
ob was visibly moved, and I told him grimly of the
eputation of the coastal road below us.

'The locals call it the Road of Death. On the stretch
rom here to Malaga, on average, somebody is killed
very day.'

We had to wait for twenty minutes before the road was
leared sufficiently for us to be able to continue our
ourney. We carried on a lively conversation on every
opic, except the grisly scene of carnage that lay before
is. In answer to my questions, Rudi told me that he and
Jalya had come to the coast to look for a house. Both of
hem were enthusiastic golfers, and Marbella is noted for
he quantity and quality of its golf courses. Rudi was a
uccessful photographer and was semi-retired. He had
ravelled a lot, but was in the fortunate situation of having
nade enough money to be able to choose where and
when he would work.

'And what about you?' I asked Bob.

'I'm afraid that I have not had an interesting life like
Rudi,' Bob said apologetically. 'I used to work in New
York; then I had a business in California.'

'What sort of business are you in?' Rudi wanted to
know.

'I'm not actually in business any more,' Bob explained.
'When I got to the States, I worked at all sorts of jobs
before I managed to set up on my own, as a supplier to
the steel industry.'

'So, where were you before?' Valya joined in.

'Budapest. I was in the uprising of 1956, and managed
to escape. You see, I had often thought about the United
States after I had been rescued by Americans at the end
of the War.'

'Rescued?' I queried.

'I was in a concentration camp,' was the quiet reply.

'And now you have retired, like Rudi?'

'No, Xaviera. I'm not sure if you will understand, but after working like mad for twenty years I got very dissatisfied with my life. I had a wife and three children but somehow I felt unfulfilled. I gave it all up and quit my family. I got myself enrolled at a university and took a course in psychology.'

'Did it work out?' I asked.

'It must have done,' Bob smiled. 'The university appointed me as a lecturer. As a matter of fact, that is how I came to meet Sharon. She was one of my most devoted students.'

'That's right,' Sharon assented. 'And we have been wonderfully happy ever since, haven't we, darling?' She pressed half a dozen kisses on his hand, leaving a pattern of red lipstick.

Bob nodded. 'We spend our weekends together, but I guess that we both enjoy our freedom too much to ever marry again.'

Sharon looked disappointed but said nothing more. However, I was intrigued by the story which we had coaxed out of Bob.

'I see,' I remarked. 'But you don't think that you have led a particularly interesting life, Bob?'

He did not answer. I felt a wave of warm sympathy for this modest, unassuming man. He was the sort of person with whom I could have a very deep relationship. Another one of those intellectually able, sensitive Jewish men who kept coming into my life! And he was an attractive looking man in his mid-fifties with strong, rugged features and wavy brown hair. His bushy eyebrows resembled deep question marks. What I liked most about his appearance was his soft brown eyes that seemed full of compassion and romantic yearning. And yet he appeared to be quite content with his new life – or so he said.

Valya broke the silence. 'I wonder what George and David are doing now. It's a pity that they could not come with us.'

'I suppose they are getting laid somewhere,' I answered.

'You can't mean that.' Valya was shocked. 'Anyone can see that they are both in love with you. They wouldn't be unfaithful, would they?'

'Why not?' I retorted. 'After all, I love both of them, and I screw around, so why shouldn't they be just as free to enjoy themselves? People come to this part of the world to have fun; they leave their worries at home.'

'That's right. You are a completely liberated woman. Love can only be found in perfect freedom.' Sharon gazed anxiously at Bob, and I felt that her remark was something which she had read in a textbook. She was one of those women who had reached her middle forties but tried to look twenty years younger. In contrast to the elegance of Valya, with her finely drawn features, Sharon had just that shade too much make-up, and her clothes were so casual that they were obviously carefully contrived. There was about her that tension of the American woman who is always seeking security, perhaps in philosophy or some way-out religion. But the more Sharon talked of sexual freedom, the more upset Valya became.

'You cannot be serious,' she protested. 'Nobody could possibly be happy with a set-up like that. It's unnatural and superficial. Look at Rudi and me. We have been perfectly happy living together for twenty-five years.'

'I don't consider any behaviour unnatural, if it gives

true pleasure,' I replied. 'Don't you think that your attitude is a bit old-fashioned? People are all different, you know. Some ought to have children; for others it would be catastrophic. Many men and women need to live together, but there are quite a few who prefer a celibate existence, and do we have the right to label somebody as unnatural simply because he or she wants to live with a companion of the same gender?'

Valya shook her head. 'You mean what people call lesbians? That's pure fantasy, isn't it? I mean, it's all very well reading about it in books, but it does not exist in real life, does it?'

I found it difficult to keep a straight face, but Valya was almost painfully sincere, and I am sure that to this day she is convinced that I was inventing things in order to shock her. Sharon, meanwhile, purred approval and attempted to enhance her girlish charms by applying a thick layer of blood-red varnish to her long, claw-like nails.

Eventually we were able to resume our journey. Soon the miniature town of Casares came into view, miraculously located, as if it had been dropped from the sky on to the mountain top, and its tiny, white-walled houses seemed to belong to the clouds rather than to the earth below. We parked the car and walked through the steep streets, unspoiled by tourist shops, until we reached the church, which crowned the very summit of the town. There was a magnificent panorama of Casares from the tranquil cemetery which surrounded the church, and we pushed open the centuries-old, timber gate. It creaked on its rusty hinges, as if to complain against our intrusion. All around were weathered stone monuments and moss-covered gravestones. When we had approached the church the streets had been completely deserted, and I

160

could not resist the spooky impression that we were indeed in a town of the dead, and that all the men and women who had ever inhabited Casares were resting in this silent churchyard. Our feet crunched on the gravel of the path: we did not speak a word, as if we feared that the slightest sound might disturb the eternal rest of those who were laid in the earth around us.

We reached the iron rail which fenced off the cemetery from the precipitous drop to the brown roof tiles below. At once, there was a change in the atmosphere of the place. A wild wind from the mountains howled at us, whipping dust up into our eyes, and bringing an eerie menace to the peaceful spot. I could not help shivering at this sudden malevolence, but unintentionally I was responsible for shattering the mood. Rudi had automatically taken out his camera and took a photograph of the rest of us as we stood by the rail. At the very moment that he pressed the shutter there was a particularly violent gust of wind, and my wrap-around dress billowed up, almost covering my head. It was a very hot day, the dress was flimsy, and I was not wearing any underwear. Of course, the incident was unrehearsed, but I noticed the flash of interest in Bob's eyes at the glimpse of my evenly tanned body. Sharon noticed too. She leaped to my side and frenziedly threw off her tank-top, exhibiting to all the world her somewhat pendulous breasts.

'That's wild,' she shouted. 'Take me too!'

I was struck by the sense of insecurity which must have been at the root of such an exhibition, and Bob looked on with distaste as Rudi obliged. Valya took me aside and confided to me that poor Rudi, being a photographer, was always having to put up with naked women throwing themselves at him, but that he never succumbed to temptation. That paragon overheard himself being

161

praised, and nodded at me uncertainly, but there was a glint in his eye which made me wonder if Valya's blind trust in his fidelity was completely justified, especially as she was busy narrating to me how she had left her spouse alone with a very attractive nude model for a whole afternoon, without the slightest qualm.

We left the church and its cemetery to those citizens of Casares who were reposing in the stony ground, and strolled around the quaint town. We cooled ourselves with drinks on the terrace of an unpretentious bar, and then drove back to Marbella.

I contrived it so that Bob sat beside me, and while we chatted I could sense Sharon's eyes boring into the back of my neck. It was evident to me that Bob found me sexually interesting, and he casually stroked my neck and fondled my leg. Presumably, since Sharon claimed to be totally liberated, she would not find anything objectionable in his attention.

That afternoon Rudi and Valya were busy with their quest for a house, Sharon took some time off for her own brand of yoga, and Bob and I, after playing a game of tennis, went back to his apartment. Sharon was still immersed in her deep meditation, so Bob and I, hot and sweaty after our game, decided to take a shower together. This had the effect of bringing Sharon rapidly out of her trance-like state. She followed us, chattering nervously, but she did not attempt to join us in the shower.

The sting of the cold water on our heated flesh was stimulating, and I definitely approved of Bob's good, strong body and big circumcised cock. When he soaped my body he got a fine hard-on, and I felt like fucking him on the spot. But when I thought of poor, possessive Sharon, and what she must be suffering outside, I could not help feeling a sense of guilt. Maybe I would not have

162

been that happy if I had thought that my boyfriend was being seduced in my own shower, by some woman whom I had not even invited round. I guess that I must have a conscience after all. So I grabbed a towel and strode out of the shower, leaving Bob startled and with a monumental erection. In the kitchen I found Sharon, practically in tears, and I reassured her that nothing more than a harmless flirtation had taken place.

We went into the bedroom, and when Bob joined us he put on a pair of immaculate yellow shorts, and Sharon, in sexy Bermuda shorts and without her make-up and false eyelashes looked, if not beautiful, at least fresher and younger. Bob sat opposite me on the bed, the soles of our feet touching. Under Sharon's unsuspecting nose, we played a super-sensual game of footsie. Very few men understand that a woman's feet are not there merely for her to stand on, but that they are a very erogenous part of her body, and that having her feet caressed or her toes sucked is a great turn-on. Bob knew. While we carried on a light conversation, our toes played to and fro, brushing against each other, and the sensation was almost as good as fucking.

Sharon was nervously thumbing a Spanish TV guide, and trying to look as if she could not care less what we might be up to. I knew that she was definitely not my type, and that she would never be ready for sex with another woman. But, from what Bob had said to me during our tennis match, I was aware that she was no longer his type either. He had never actually been in love with Sharon, but he had friendly feelings towards her, and she had been so desperate that he had allowed himself to become entangled with her, rather than have her believe that he had let her down. The fascination of her devotion had soon worn off, but now she was driving him crazy, as perhaps she had done to her three departed husbands. She never left him free for a weekend, and it was for that reason that he had decided to take a break on his own in Spain. Sharon had found out, and took the next flight to Malaga. The unhappy woman knew that she could not own or control her man, and simply could not cope. So much for her fine talk of liberation and total freedom; no wonder she needed yoga!

We met for dinner that night at David's apartment. David listened to an account of our trip to Casares, but I wanted to hear what he had been doing.

'Where have you been,' I demanded, 'and with whom?'

'Do you really imagine that I would be out with some other woman when you are in town, Xaviera?'

'What did I tell you!' Valya cried triumphantly.

I ignored her and continued my interrogation. 'Were you with a girl?'

'Of course I was,' David laughed. 'I took her up to the mountains also, but made sure that we went in a different direction from you. Did I never mention Amalia to you?' he added with an air of assumed innocence.

'I think that I could count the number of your conquests on the fingers of one hand, with the thumb shot off,' I replied, 'but for some reason, the name Amalia escapes me.'

'It happened because I decided that I ought to learn Spanish.' David had long learned to ignore my sarcasms. 'The only foolproof method was to acquire a Spanish girlfriend, in a bar. That's what bars are for,' he explained. 'So, I met Amalia. You would like her: she's quite pretty, apart from her face, if you understand me. She speaks not one word of English and her Spanish is pure Andalucian, so when I thought that she professed her undying love, maybe she said something else. Still, we made a date, and to my surprise she turned up here as arranged, not more than twenty minutes late. I kissed her tenderly but I won't bore you with the details of what happened when I led her towards the bed.'

'Did you fuck her?' I asked impatiently.

'Don't be indelicate,' David rebuked me. 'She wept and assured me that it was quite impossible, but that in two days' time she would be mine. I understood that the poor girl must be having her period, so I did not insist. She used my phone to call her mother, who was in Madrid, and by the time she had finished, we had an hour or so to pass before she had to get back to the bar where she worked. "But in two days," I repeated. She assured me that by then she would have had some hair removed from her legs. She pulled up her trouser leg, and I saw where she required some depilatory treatment, but I felt cheated.'

'Where did you take her?'

'It would be more accurate to say that she took me, Xaviera. We drove to Ojen to visit a Canadian girlfriend of hers. The man who designed that road never had a Rolls Royce in mind. Ojen is nice, though not as pretty as Casares, but the road twists and turns and goes on for ever. I had not filled the car, and we were getting dangerously low on petrol by the time we arrived. The Canadian was not in, and I told Amalia that I needed to find a service station. Amalia knew that there was one, just up the road, so instead of turning back towards civilization, we pressed on. The road got even worse, and there was no sign of a garage, or any trace of human habitation. I found that we were heading towards a place aptly called Monda. I was now quite convinced that we were approaching the end of the world, and round the next bend of the road we would fall off.

'Amalia had been to Monda, and she knew that we could buy petrol there. Finally, we arrived at the untidy huddle of shanties, the church and the village store, which comprised Monda. When I saw the place, my heart sank, Amalia asked a man in the street, but he shook his head and informed us that there was nowhere in Monda where anybody could buy petrol. I got the impression that the "town" was bereft of motor transport, and the need had never previously arisen. Dismay gave way to resignation. We could never get back to Marbella, and would perish up in the mountains, among the aboriginal inhabitants of this forgotten corner of the planet.

'By now, the car had been surrounded by a horde of young children, who gazed at us in amazement and fingered the coachwork to make sure that it was real. Suddenly, an earnest-faced eight-year-old piped up, "Excuse me, Sir, but do you speak English?" His accent was impeccable. I stared at this incarnation of Little Lord Fauntleroy. "Young man, you are the very person I want to see. Can you kindly direct me to the nearest garage?" The kid considered, and reluctantly shook his head. A shriller treble joined in. "I know," said his six-year-old sister. Well, they argued: the girl was the only person in the place who believed that she knew where we could buy some petrol, and I ended up by taking the two of them on board, and following her directions. It seemed futile, but I had no alternative. She directed me through a maze of alleys, rather than streets, and I began to visualize the car getting jammed, like a cork in a bottle. All hope had perished, and the boy was pouring aristocratic scorn on our pilot, when she cried out, "Here we are." We were outside a dilapidated house. Incredibly, the old woman who lived there sold cans of gasoline, an inferior grade, but it was the elixir of life for me.

166

'Amalia was by now overwhelmed by the charm of the children, and much to their embarrassment, wept copiously over them. She thrust a hundred-peseta note into the boy's hand, and kissed him. He turned to me and said, "Excuse me, Sir, may I have a few words with you?" From his expression, I thought that perhaps he had mistaken me for Amalia's father, and was about to request her hand in marriage. Outside the car, he pointed out that he considered a hundred pesetas rather a large sum, and did not wish to take advantage of the lady. I assured him that he could accept the money with a clear conscience, and the unlikely pair politely wished us a good journey, and took their leave.

'On the road back, I gave Amalia a hundred-peseta note, to repay her for what she had given our benefactors. Indignantly, she pushed the money back into my hand. "Do you think I am a prostitute?" she flared up. "I gave the money because I loved those children. It was my own money and I do what I like with it." She was so annoyed that she never said another word to me all the way back to Marbella, and when we left she made it clear that she considered our date in a couple of days' time as null and void.'

'When David is not telling long, tedious stories,' I said to Bob, 'he plays the piano quite well. Why don't we get him to play something?'

We all urged him to oblige, so David went over to the keyboard, and launched into the opening bars of a Beethoven sonata. I was astounded by the reactions of our visitors. Sharon sat, clasping her toes, apparently in a trance, and when Valya, who was smoking a cigarette, asked for an ashtray, Sharon commanded silence. Bob was looking straight ahead, but his eyes were full of tears.

When the music was over, Sharon dug him in the ribs and asked him what was the matter with him.

'It's such a beautiful piece,' Valya commented. 'It must have brought back some tender memory; a romantic meeting with a lovely woman, perhaps?'

'A very unhappy memory,' Bob corrected her. 'In the concentration camp, where we were awaiting being shipped on, we were joined by a group of Hungarian Jews, among whom were two children, both of them prodigies. There was a piano and they were allowed to play: you know how sentimental the Germans can be over music. The girl would always perform sonatas of Beethoven. I can remember her now, with her long hair and soft, trusting brown eyes, in her early teens, a child about to mature into a woman. They had no idea that they were destined for Auschwitz.

'Several years after the War had ended, I was in New York, when I saw the name of the boy pianist on a poster. He was giving a recital at Carnegie Hall. I bought a ticket, and at the end went backstage and asked him what had happened to the girl. I think I knew what he was going to answer. "Very few of us got out alive," he whispered. He did not need to finish the sentence. She was so lovely and so talented, the first woman I ever fell in love with, and she never knew. She could have charmed the stars out of the sky. I ask you, why did the brutes have to destroy her? The sonata that David just played was the last music she played, before they took her away to be tortured and slaughtered.'

There was nothing to be said after that. David got up and put on a record of a Schubert Quintet. We listened in silence, Sharon in her strange, mystic posture. Before long, she began to snore. I took advantage of her slumber to make a date with Bob to visit me at my own apartment, and I shall never forget the gentleness of the touch of his fingers, when we made love.

The music stopped and Rudi got to his feet. He explained that it was getting late, and that he and Valya had to be on the golf course early in the morning. He stated this as if it were one of the laws of nature and a self-evident truth. Valya shook her head as she prepared to leave.

'I still don't understand the relationship between you and David,' she confessed to me.

'There's no mystery,' David said. 'Xaviera does whatever she likes, and so do I. That way, we get along very well.'

Valya was still shaking her head like a baffled animal when she left. The door closing woke up Sharon.

She stretched and yawned. 'It's marvellous the way music can relax you, when you really concentrate,' she informed us.

'That's right,' David agreed. 'And I believe that it is even better when you are awake.'

As I drove home, my thoughts were on Bob, his story and our forthcoming meeting. His sensitive yet strong face haunted me. Another Jewish man with a problem, I thought. It always happens with me: I have to straighten their heads first, before I can get to their cocks.

17
Nothing is for Nothing

Next day I was busy looking up old friends, but that evening George and I went out to dinner with David. I had told George about some of the bizarre exploits of David's neighbour, Alfonso. I was certain that I had not heard half of their misadventures, so while we sat back over our coffees, I steered the conversation round to David's expedition to the mountains of the previous day.

'I'm surprised that you did not take Alfonso with you,' I commented. 'You did use him for an alibi; do I take it that he has been providing you with plenty of action through the long winter months?'

'Alfonso!' David snorted. 'He wouldn't score at a nymphomaniac's invitation ball on a leap year. For weeks he promised impending triumphs in the war of the sexes, but I guess we were permanently in the strategic reserve, never in the front line. There was the time we met Anita, for example.'

'Tell me all,' I cajoled, knowing that he would anyway.

'It started, like all Alfonso's evenings, in a bar,' David told us. 'We were there for the first and last time. It was a dismal place, where the barman was as faded as the wallpaper, and the only other occupant was helping us to prop the bar up. Alfonso was engaged in his favourite pastime, describing imaginary women and his fictitious conquests. When I complained of the absence of all these flashing eyes and thighs, in the flesh as it were, Alfonso's excuse was that during the winter there were no chicks in town. That was when the stranger intervened. "Would you guys be interested in going to another bar, where the booze is drinkable, and there are some luscious girls in attendance?" I could not believe my ears. He looked like an ordinary mortal, and he did not appear to be carrying a magic wand.

'Our saviour said that he had recently opened this fabulous bar, and if we cared to drop in and say that he had sent us, we would be presented with a free drink, and made more than welcome. "Real whisky," he assured us, "not like the piss you get here." The barman nodded his agreement with that sentiment, so we lost no time in hitting the trail for El Dorado.

'You know the name El Dorado was often scrawled on ancient charts, but mariners found it impossible to put an exact location on the land of untold riches. Let me assure you that despite the marvels of modern technology, the problem still defies solution. Of course, we had been given the address of the bar, and even a rough diagram of how to get there, but when we followed these directions, we found ourselves a few hundred metres beyond the end of the main road and the street lamps, at a heap of rubble. It looked the ideal spot to accommodate an avalanche, an epidemic, or even an inferior class of abattoir, but hardly the site of an exotic, sexy, "with it" bar. I cursed Alfonso, quietly but fluently. With his local knowledge, he suggested a couple of roads with similar names which we then explored. Fifty minutes later, having rejected a furniture shop and a fish restaurant, we were back at the same frontier of the civilized world, with Alfonso poring over the diagram. I was ready to give up and go home, but Alfonso pointed to some ramshackle buildings at the bottom of something more like a goat track than a footpath. He insisted that we should explore, and I went along simply to humour the lunatic. And that is how we

171

stumbled across El Dorado, about twenty metres back from a concealed side road.

'To be fair to the place, it boasted a neon sign, cunningly placed so as to be invisible from the road. Alfonso was revoltingly self-righteous as he pushed open the door, and we entered the palace of delights. It was not at all what we had been led to expect. There was a counter and a long line of bottles on a shelf, so we concluded that it was, indeed, a bar. The subdued lighting was due to the fact that most of the bulbs had burned out, and the decor was not so much plushy as moth-eaten. The only female present smiled at us from behind the counter. She was a tall, tough-looking blonde, and I presumed that she was waiting for a girlfriend, since she was wearing make-up for two.

We explained that we had been invited, and ordered a couple of whiskies. The barmaid nodded understandingly, served the drinks and demanded four hundred pesetas. When we protested, she explained that the rule of the house was that the second drink was free. I suppose we were weak-willed, but we paid up. We were very thirsty after our long quest, and I was curious to see what excuse she would produce when we came to order our second drink.

Alfonso, the soul of tact, asked bluntly where all the girls were, to which the answer came that we should hang around because it was still early. As we sipped our whisky, which tasted like an inferior version of the brew which had been so roundly condemned in the first bar, I became aware of the presence of another human being. It resembled a satirical caricature of a woman, and smiled invitingly as it slid on to the stool next to mine.

'I gazed at her in disbelief. Could this be the angel who had been despatched to minister to our physical yearn-ngs? Her scanty attire made it abundantly clear that she was a mammal and a biped. I looked at her face, and shuddered, but she waved her orange locks at me encouragingly, and when she crossed her legs, I was made to realize that she regarded panties as an irrelevant luxury. "Buy me a drink," hissed the harpy. I winced at the vice-like grip of her talon on my thigh, and as she was sitting between me and the door, I complied and ordered three whiskies. Alfonso hesitantly reminded the barmaid that two of them were on the house. This time, the bill was three hundred pesetas. I pointed out that a whisky only cost two hundred pesetas five minutes ago. The barmaid was very patient with me, explaining to the untutored that our companion, as a "bar-girl", received a payment for every drink she could entice out of us. "I know that," I told her indignantly, "the bar gives her a commission, not the customer." Apparently this bar was an exception.

'Enlightenment dawned. "So, if I were to buy a drink for myself, it would cost two hundred?" The barmaid, like a school teacher with a backward pupil, agreed. I grabbed the whisky before the resident vampire could take the glass. "All three whiskies are for my friend and myself. Two of them are free, so we are square," I said, as I placed two hundred pesetas on the counter. Before the "bar-girl" had a chance to protest, I pushed one of the glasses towards her. "Do let me give you one of my drinks," I invited.

'That was how we got out of there with no more damage than perforated eardrums from the imprecations which pursued us.'

'And her name was Anita?' I enquired.

'Good heavens, no. Whatever gave you that idea? Anita was in the next bar. You see, we had to stop for a drink to get over our horrible experience. Alfonso was rebuking me for attempted misconduct with the black widow, when he stopped in mid-sentence, his eyes glazed and his nostrils started to quiver. There could only be one possible explanation. A young girl had just entered and taken a seat at a table. With the sly subtlety of a charging rhinoceros, he joined her and offered her a drink. After our last encounter, any woman would have looked like Helen of Troy, but she was actually attractive. She was dark and trim, and looked clean and well mannered. Not at all the sort of girl for Alfonso, I thought, and as if to endorse my opinion, she refused his offer.

Not that she was unfriendly. Alfonso engaged her in a very one-sided conversation, which continued for half an hour, but from which the following points emerged. Her name was Anita, she was Swiss and had only arrived that day and she proposed to stay on the coast for three weeks. She had no friends in the place, but she preferred to pay for her own Cokes, and she was quite comfortable in her hotel. That was in answer to Alfonso's invitation to her to visit my flat – he would come too. She also informed him that she had no desire to be shown around the town and that as she had an appointment back at her hotel, she would have to be leaving.

Alfonso was exultant. Once the heat got to work on her, he told me, she would drop that hard-to-get pose. I objected that he had omitted to ask her where she was staying, but he waved aside my objection. She would come back to the same bar: they always do. "She will be here, looking for me," announced the monument to male vanity. As she was obviously a very respectable young lady, it would have been unreasonable to expect her to capitulate at their first meeting. It was getting late, and I suggested that we go home, and that he take a cold bath, but he insisted that we stop at yet one more bar on the road, to celebrate his conquest.

It was quiet, and the only feature of the place which marked it out from all the other bars was an alcove, screened off by a heavy curtain, opposite the counter. Alfonso had wandered off to find a toilet, and he peered into the alcove on his way back. I downed my nightcap and urged the wretch to hurry, so that we could get back to bed. But Alfonso was in a strangely leisurely mood, and as we had come in his car, I had to restrain my impatience. He even started paying for drinks, and found one excuse after another to delay our departure. I was resigned to our staying at the bar for a late breakfast, but after an hour and a half Alfonso agreed to leave.

'"Well," I demanded petulantly, "what was all that about?" He smiled sardonically. "When I went for a pèe, I was able to see into that alcove. There was a guy with his trousers unzipped, and a girl was giving him a good time, if you know what I mean." I was surprised by his unusual reticence, but assured him that I got the picture. Now he mentioned the alcove, I recollected that I had fancied that I had heard some rustling from behind the curtain, but had not given the matter any attention. "The girl saw me go past, but she could not tell whether I had seen her – and recognized her. It was your innocent little Anita," Alfonso continued gleefully. I noted how suddenly she had become my property.

Alfonso had resented the coolness of her earlier behaviour and decided that she should be taught a lesson. By hanging about, he had ensured that her customer got value for money, since she would not want us to see her, and would wait for us to leave before she emerged. Keeping her bottled up in the alcove for the rest of the night also meant that she would not have the chance to get any more clients, which amused Alfonso mightily. Of course, he claimed that he had acted to protect me from temptation. "Well, she was truthful," I pointed out. "She really did have an appointment. Not bad for someone who had only arrived in Spain that day. Anyway, she must hate you now, Alfonso; better luck next time."'

'So that was the end of your romance with Anita,' George grinned.

'Not according to Alfonso,' David answered. 'He takes the view that we now really do know where she operates, and we should go back there. After all, how could any woman resist a man with his charm, wit, good looks and with such a gallant character?'

'It's time we were on our way,' I said to George, rising from my seat. I turned to David. 'And I suppose that you are off to your bed?'

'Not yet. I am not too tired and I might just look in at a bar I got to know the other night.' He smiled and added, 'This time, without Alfonso.'

18
Viva España!

George had gone back to London, and a few days later I had the opportunity to go to a bullfight. Andalucia is where the sport originated in Spain, and the oldest *plaza de toros* is a graceful building in Ronda. I had been to fights in other countries, but this would be the first time here. I persuaded David to accompany me. He agreed reluctantly, after Alfonso had criticized him for condemning bullfighting without ever having been to a *corrida*. Pepe, a friend of Alfonso's, was much more enthusiastic, so the three of us joined the big crowd lining up to buy tickets. We tried to get seats on the shady side of the arena. They were more expensive, but they had all been taken by ticket touts, who were selling them at fancy prices. As we anticipated that there would only be about an hour's fighting, we refused to patronize the touts, but I got the impression that we then paid more for our seats, because we would be able to enjoy the sunshine.

Pepe explained to us the technicalities of the *corrida* with all the self-assurance of a Spaniard who had lived all his adult life in Germany. The show started with remarkably un-Spanish punctuality. There was a flourish of trumpets and then, to the lively strains of a *paso doble*, the participants paraded across the broad, sand-floored arena. The men strutted in their gorgeous costumes, and the horses pranced and tossed their heads, as the spectators clapped their hands and shouted encouragement.

When the procession had left the arena, the first of the bulls was let in. Its adversary was a *rejenador*, a man who fought the bull from horseback. The horse had no protective armour of any sort, and its very life depended on its agility and the intelligence of its rider. That the horse was superbly trained had been apparent from the way it danced to the music of the opening parade. Compared to the horse, with its nimble movements, the bull was a poor, lumbering beast, and it never looked as if it would be able to get its horns into the flanks of its tormentor. It blundered from one side of the arena to the other, until it was despatched with clinical precision. The *rejenador* excited the spectators to polite rather than exuberant applause. The crowd admired his skill, but it would take something more primitive to stir them. He had been too accomplished to arouse in them the sensation of actual danger.

The other bulls were fought in the more customary manner, but I felt that we never saw a true, one to one combat; a man pitting his skill and courage alone against the ferocity of a bull. Before the *matador* entered the arena, the bull, a heavily built, black beast, was teased and confused by a regiment of men, standing close to a sturdily built wall, who waved their brightly coloured capes at it, and hastily jumped over the wall whenever the exasperated beast charged in their direction. Occasionally the bull was able to get one man in a corner, but then it would be distracted by some of his comrades.

There was a purpose behind all the preliminary cape play. It enabled the *matador* to observe the bull, and see from which side it would habitually charge. The men who did give me my first thrill were those who sprinted across the arena and, under the very horns of the infuriated bull, planted their *banderillas* in the muscles at the back of its neck. If one of them had tripped, or was a shade slow on his feet, nothing could have saved him from being sav-ged, and his body being broken by the brute strength of he bull. But they all made it, though some had to make a second or even a third run before they were able to sink heir ribboned darts into the animal, which looked as if it had been adorned for some ritual sacrifice.

For me, the arrival of the *picador* was an anticlimax. Seated on a horse which was blinkered and protected by a huge basketwork bustle, which no bull could possibly penetrate, he repeatedly thrust a massive pointed lance into the side of the bull. Long streaks of blood flowed down the animal's flanks, as it tried vainly to charge the heavily-armoured horse, but the *picador* went on stabbing remorselessly. Pepe had said that this was to infuriate the bull, but it was clear that, in this fight at any rate, the aim of the *picador* was to so weaken the animal that it would be an easy prey for the *matador*. The crowd sensed this and began to grow restive. Their shouts were no longer of praise, but of protest. Yet there was something fascinating about this cold, relentless torture which made me shiver.

The bull was weak and shaken before the *matador* stood before it, with cape and sword. The hubbub of the crowd died down to a sullen silence. The wounded animal gathered its remaining strength to rush at the *matador*, and after a few desultory passes with his cape, he prepared to deliver the *coup de grâce*. As the bull charged, the *matador* stabbed, over the horns, straight into the heart. At least, that was the way it should have been done, but in this particular fight everything was done with gory clumsiness. The *matador* three times missed the vital spot and the end was botched and messy. The crowd howled, hissed and booed, and they registered their disgust and disapproval by throwing cushions into the arena.

Fortunately, not all the bouts were so badly executed. What intrigued me was that when the sword thrust was true, piercing the heart of the bull, the animal would still go on charging. Then, quite suddenly, it would stumble to its knees, and slowly die before our eyes. It was an eerie spectacle.

Only the last fight was carried out with real style. The *picador* restricted himself to his proper role, and the *matador* faced a worthy adversary, strong and vicious, with cool daring. The mood changed immediately. This is what the people had come to see, and I could feel the mounting tension. As the duel reached its inevitable climax, I found that I was gripping David's hand so tight that my nails bit deeply into his flesh. I was so carried away by the drama that, at the moment when the human actor made that one, short, deadly stab, I screamed and shuddered, as I experienced a strange, sinister form of orgasm.

Later, Alfonso asked whether David had been converted.

'I was not so much overwhelmed by sympathy for the bulls,' he answered, 'as appalled by the way the onlookers deteriorated into a mob, howling for blood. They did not want to applaud agility and courage, only to see death. The way they were screaming "*Matalo!*" [kill him] brought home to me that the men had become more bestial than the so-called beast.'

I did not take such an extreme view as David, but the fight had made me conscious of what a land of contrasts Spain is. Just as the blinding sunlight plunges everything into stark relief, glaring white or the sheer blackness of shadows, destroying all the subtle gradations of colour, so it is with human passions. Spain is a country of violent emotions, of love and death. What I did not realize was how soon I was to witness, at first hand, this tension of Spanish love, and Spanish death.

I had invited Betty to come back to Marbella this year, and spend a few weeks with me. Her previous visit had been marred by some problems, but that was in the past, and I was genuinely looking forward to seeing her again. She duly arrived, and installed herself in my apartment. But it was not long before the intimacy of our cosy menage was disturbed.

The previous summer I had met a gay boy, Andrew, who designed subtle and refined jewellery, and Betty was with me when I went to his shop and bought a few things. The last thing I expected was an affair between the gay boy and the lesbian girl, but she lost no time before ringing him up, and Andrew became a constant visitor.

Although I liked Andrew, it was perfectly obvious to me that he was headstrong, capricious, and very, very spoilt. Fair, slim and tall, he had good looks which appealed to men and women alike, and he had that self-confidence which often comes from an English public school education. He preferred older men and was living with Carlos, a Spaniard of about forty-five, and rumoured to be something of a recluse. I learned that Carlos doted on Andrew. Whenever they quarrelled, Andrew only had to threaten to leave, and Carlos would collapse abjectly. He gave Andrew anything he asked for, and became utterly dependent on the young Englishman. They were rarely seen together, but Andrew would often be out, flirting with young boys, while Carlos stayed at home and fretted.

All this I learned from Andrew himself, when he came to my apartment. His behaviour towards me was always courteous and correct, but there was a much stronger bond of sympathy between him and Betty. They were both creative artists and had a lot in common: I suppose, in retrospect, that I ought to have taken notice of how

181

girlish Andrew was, with his little piques and changes of mood, and foreseen how his temperament would attract the boyish Betty. But it is easy to be wise after the event.

One day, when the three of us were about to go out together, I suggested that Andrew invite Carlos to join us.

'Good Lord, no!' he laughed. 'You would not enjoy his company. He is a raging hysteric and a drunk – and not even good-looking. What a slob!'

'So why do you stay with him, if he is so objectionable?' I asked.

'Well, it's a roof over my head,' Andrew answered. 'And a pretty nice roof, at that. I can do whatever I like, and I don't think that poor old Carlos would survive if I walked out. I shout at him a lot, but, you know, that's what he really enjoys, being bossed about, although I must admit that it does drive him to the bottle, and his liver is in bad shape.'

I wondered whether Andrew was gratifying genuine masochistic yearnings in Carlos, or whether he was not inflicting great unhappiness on him. Maybe Carlos could not cope and needed help, and I resolved to get in touch with him and see if with my fund of experience, I could assist him in freeing himself from an unwelcome subjection.

But that good intention had to be shelved for a while because of the arrival in Marbella of Angelique, a French-woman living in Barcelona, who was a reporter with a leading Spanish newspaper group, and who had come to the coast in order to interview me. I liked the look of her as soon as she walked in. A vivacious redhead of about forty, she was clearly a woman of strong character and, judging from her clothes, good taste. The interview took an hour, and then I prepared a meal for the two of us.

182

While I cooked, she talked. In fact, she never stopped talking. I learned that she was yet another lesbian, and I realized that she was highly intelligent and obviously sexually aware, but how I wished that she would give her voice a rest for a moment! She was the sort of woman who could talk any man soft, if she had been into guys. Of course, while I had my hands full with Angelique, Betty and Andrew were away together.

The night that Betty had arrived, I had not been feeling at all horny. I had already started writing something which was eventually to become this book, and at such times I would often sublimate my sexual energy in work, so I did not make love to her. Several evenings later we went to one of the local discotheques, called Rocky, but I was very tired and decided to go home early to get some rest, leaving Betty, to whom I had given her own key, with Andrew. I took a hot drink and drifted into a deep sleep, from which I was aroused at nearly four in the morning by the phone ringing.

I groped for the phone, but when I answered, the caller hung up without saying a word. A few minutes later the same thing happened again, and I suspected that I was the victim of a silly practical joke. There were several more false alarms, and I was pretty furious, when a man finally responded to my demanding who the hell was on the line.

'Is Andrew with you?' he asked, in a heavily accented voice.

I did not have to be a detective to be able to identify my caller as Carlos, and from his slurred tones, it was clear that he was very drunk. I was on the verge of shouting at him for waking me up, but for some reason I let him ramble on, and as I listened, my annoyance turned to pity. He knew nothing about Betty, and suspected me

183

of trying to have an affair with his boyfriend and to threaten his homosexuality. Insanely jealous, he had followed us to Rocky, but frightened of upsetting Andrew, he had not dared to go in. Instead, he had returned to his house to wait for him to come home. Although he had been drinking, he did not give me the impression that he was the hopeless boor that Andrew had described, and he certainly was not stupid, despite being frantic with worry and jealousy. I managed to convince him that I had no designs on Andrew, and that he would be far better able to handle his problem with his lover in the morning if we both got some sleep. By then he had become quite reasonable, so I proposed that we meet for dinner the next day. Meanwhile, I advised him to go easy on the boy when he did get back: I knew that if there were to be a showdown it would be Carlos, not Andrew, who would suffer.

At ten in the morning, Betty returned, took a bath, washed her hair and, after drinking some orange juice, was ready to go out again to meet Andrew for a game of paddle tennis. She said that I could join them, but her tone was such that I was sure that I would not be welcome, and I went into town to meet Angelique. During the afternoon, I had another phone conversation with Carlos, now perfectly sober, in which he told me that Andrew had finally crawled in, looking like a wet rag, and commanded Carlos to make him some breakfast, but had refused to say where he had been and what he had been doing. However, I knew, since by then Betty had given me a blow by blow account.

'You know, seducing a gay guy is quite a challenge,' she gloated. 'You ought to try it sometime, Xaviera. You could find it a totally new experience.'

I declined to comment, and Betty smiled condescendingly as she went on to enlighten me.

'After you had gone home, we stayed on for a while at the disco, and I could tell that Andrew was in the mood for some excitement, so I suggested that I should find him a nice boy, if he pulled me a good, juicy girl. He liked the idea, but all that was available was a sweet little Swedish teenager, called Grete, who made it obvious that she fancied me. The three of us ended up in an apartment which she had rented.

'The chick was raring to go, but poor Andrew had no idea what it was all about and was as nervous as a kitten. He had never seen a couple of women make love, so I told him that he should watch us as he might learn a thing or two. I made him sit on a chair in front of us, while I took Grete's clothes off and admired her fine, firm breasts, and her pretty bush of pubic hair, not too much, just the way I like it. Her skin was clear and lovely to touch; when I stroked her, she closed her big blue eyes and literally purred. But I gave her a great working over, licking her breasts and fondling her clit, while she turned and twisted all over the bed and ran her fingers through my hair. All the time Andrew sat there, with his eyes popping out of his head. We ignored him completely, and that seemed to turn him on more than ever.

'Then I looked up at him and ordered him to strip. He had to obey me, and next I made him lie on the floor at our feet and masturbate. Grete was frantic by now, and I slid my body over her, so that she could eat my pussy. She was soaking wet, and had a strong, sensual smell. I commanded Andrew to get on his knees and kiss her cunt and eat her. He buried his head in her groin. It did not take him long to learn what he had to do, and Grete came three times before she wanted a pause. By now, Andrew had an erection like the Eiffel Tower, but although he pleaded with me, I would not let him come.

'Grete was lying on her side, gently fingering herself. "Now do the same to me," I directed him. The state that he was in, he would have had to do whatever I dictated. I suppose that with Carlos, he is the dominant partner, but with us, he was merely a slave. He has a good, firm tongue, and I soon had him working the way I wanted, but when Grete came up behind him, and slipped one of her fingers in his asshole, he went absolutely crazy. Even then, I refused to let him come, although he was on the brink three or four times. Only when he was absolutely desperate, I grabbed him hard and told him to fuck me.

'You know, Xaviera, only once in a while I fancy a man, but he has to be the right type, and Andrew was fine, firm but yet gentle. All the time that he was inside me, Grete never took her finger out, and he was in a frenzy. I would not let him finish until I had enjoyed one superb orgasm, and I gripped him tight with my legs, so that he could not move his swollen, tormented cock while I throbbed against it. Only then did I relax the pressure on him, and he came at once, without any climax, just lying there helpless, unable to move, and leaking sperm all over Grete's bed. For quite some time he was in a state of shock. In fact, I don't know if sweet little Andrew will ever be the same again. All those cunts and tits have got him very confused.'

I restrained my anger until Betty had completed her triumphant narrative. Then, in a quiet, controlled voice, I informed her of Carlos's calls during the night. She merely shrugged her shoulders.

'So what has that got to do with me?'

'Good God!' I exploded. 'How selfish can you be? We were lovers, now I am beginning to doubt whether we are

186

even friends. You know well enough that I don't sleep a lot, but I do need my rest, so why should I have to be disturbed because of your fooling about? And what about Carlos and Andrew? They had a steady relationship before you interfered. Have you thought what damage you are doing? It is not as if you really loved or cared for Andrew.'

'What I do is my own business,' she retorted. 'And what do you know of their relationship, anyway? It can't be that hot; they don't even fuck.'

'Leave them alone. It's the same as breaking up a marriage for no reason at all, apart from your need to show off. Why do you always have to be Number One?'

'Oh, shut up, and you leave me alone! I am only here for a couple of weeks, and I intend to enjoy myself.'

She picked up her bag and slung it over her shoulder. Before she could go out, I told her that I had invited Carlos to join us for dinner that evening, and that I presumed she had no objection.

'Does he have to come along?' she grumbled. 'From what Andrew has told me, he sounds a real drag.'

'This is my place, and he is my guest,' I pointed out.

She turned away and stormed out, slamming the door behind her.

David and I had arranged to go that evening to a village up in the mountains called Benahavis, where there was to be a *feria*, a local fair without any of the ballyhoo of the tourist resorts. Before that, we all assembled for dinner at a restaurant in the Port: Betty and Andrew, Angelique, whom I had asked along, David and myself, and now also Carlos. I wondered what Andrew's companion would be like, and I was pleasantly surprised. Carlos was casually dressed in sweater and jeans, but his clothes were neat and clean. He was dark and rather thick-set, with large

187

sad eyes. He had big strong hands, but I noticed how nervously he kept twisting them when he spoke, and I found out later that he had taken a stiff dose of Valium before leaving. I had half expected a scene over the meal, but everybody had calmed down, and it was left to Angelique to astonish me. She was sitting next to David, to whom she chattered incessantly.

Turning to me, with an infectious grin, she confided, 'You know, your David is very sexy. I really could do something with him.'

'But I thought that you were a lesbian,' David protested.

'Not a hundred per cent. Every now and then, I meet a man whom I truly like. You are one of the very few.' Then, beaming at him over her gazpacho, she added, 'I sure would like to rape you.'

I never found out how David would have taken to that proposition, since Angelique prattled on until any spark of lust there might have been in his loins had long been extinguished by that spate of words. The meal over, we walked back to where we had parked the cars, and then drove up the narrow, winding road to Benahavis, where the festivities were in full swing.

Down in Marbella, the *feria* was a Coney Island affair, with the broad open space clogged by dodgem cars and side shows, but up in the village there was simply a lot of singing and dancing in the square, as the Spaniards who lived there had a good time, with only a scattering of tourists in attendance. The men and women wore their everyday clothes, but the children were sumptuously dressed, especially the little girls who were resplendent in long frocks of the brightest scarlet, green or gold, and all delicately trimmed with lace. We ran into plenty of old friends and acquaintances as we pushed our way through the good-humoured crowd.

One man who tagged along with our party was an American painter named Joseph. He had lived in Spain for fifteen years, but well away from the coast, which he rarely visited. I had met him in the house of a friend the previous year, and taken a liking to him at once. The same friend had told Joseph that I was back in town and would be at the *feria* that evening, and he had made the long journey from his remote country estate specially to see me again.

He was a dynamic personality, and had the lean, sensitive features of an artist. When he spoke, there was an eagerness in his voice, as though he had been waiting a long time for the company of somebody like me. And I was more than ever pleased to have him with me. Since the departure of George, I had been almost exclusively in the company of women, what with Betty and Angelique, and I was beginning to feel that some male company would be welcome. Of course, David was about, but he had made arrangements for Marianne to come and stay with him for a while, so there would be yet another girl! Joseph danced with me, and we agreed to spend the night together at my apartment. As I anticipated, we were not burdened with the company of Betty and Andrew who were off somewhere together, while I suppose Carlos was sitting at home, waiting and agonizing, but this time without phoning me.

Relaxing in my lounge, with a drink in his hand, Joseph told me lots of things about his life which I did not know before. He had left his native New York to make films and done very well. But things seemed to come too easily to satisfy him. So, he and his family had come to Spain and made a fresh start. He had always had an ambition to become a painter, and now he was well established, with his own galleries in Marbella, New York and Toronto. He and his wife, Ruth, had been happily married for thirty years, and of their five children, only the two youngest boys still lived at home with them.

We were in a mellow frame of mind when we retired to the bedroom. To my delight, Joseph proved to be a great lover, and he was just what I needed after all the stupid, petty annoyances which I had been suffering. And I was really ready for a man! The room was lit by two tall candles which flickered in the night breeze, and the soft strains of the Chopin Nocturnes issued from the reel to reel tape recorder in the lounge. Before we undressed, Joseph pulled me to him, and kissed me tenderly. I felt all the frustrations of the day drain away, and I was wet with anticipation. Although he was no longer a young man, his skin was unwrinkled and smooth as satin to the touch. It was a relief, after hearing Betty's account of what she had done with Andrew, to be with a man who was capable of fulfilling a man's role, and Joseph did it beautifully.

He fondled my fingers and wrists which, in comparison with his, were as fragile as those of a doll. The way he touched me made me feel wonderfully feminine, and his every movement was gentle and unhurried. I adored the tenderness with which he stroked my shoulders and my neck, and I pulled the fingers of his other hand into my mouth and nibbled them with tiny, mock bites. When I curled my own fingers around his balls, and lightly ran my thumb up the proud shaft of his eager cock, a sweet smile of pleasure came over his face, and he pressed his lips hard against my mouth, forcing his tongue inside and letting it play against my own.

Eventually he entered me, and he fucked with an

190

uncanny combination of passion and control, prolonging the sensation until the moment when it was almost unbearable, and twice bringing me to an orgasm before, holding me firmly and thrusting deep inside me, he came to his own great climax. We lay back in each other's arms, letting our bodies recover and savouring their aromas, so different but both thrillingly sensual. We had no thought of sleep for we had hardly started the exploration of each other's sexuality, and we were aroused like a pair of mating animals.

If our first encounter was simple and serious, what followed was often lighthearted and at times downright hilarious. By some magic telepathy, we knew without saying a word when we were ready to resume, and spontaneously moved into a sixty-nine position, where I found that his tongue was as accomplished as his cock. He fluttered it over and around my clitoris until I seized his head and pressed it close between my thighs. He drank my love juices as if they were a precious vintage, and my orgasm was a thing of wonder. Yet, in the middle of my ecstasy, I never lost the realization of the mounting excitement of his own straining penis, and the sperm surged out into my avid mouth at the very moment that I came.

After that a longer pause was necessary, and I went into the kitchen and brought us in some cold drinks and a couple of ice creams. The drinks refreshed us, but we found novel ways of devouring the ice creams. I placed a lump of pistachio in my pussy, and Joseph ate it and me at the same time. But two can play at that game; he smeared his cock and I licked it, enjoying the combined flavours of raspberry and circumcised penis.

Eventually, our games came to an end. We were exhausted and sated with pleasure. Before we went to

191

sleep, Joseph invited me to spend the weekend at his place, with his family.

'That is, if you like animals and birds, and do not object to the rough and ready ways of country life,' he smiled. 'I warn you that the place is virtually a menagerie.'

When I reassured him that I would not mind sharing the rambling farmhouse with such occupants as a tame fox, a stable full of horses and an owl with a broken wing, he was delighted. All I needed to bring with me, so he told me, was a bikini, a pair of old jeans and some tennis sneakers. I was looking forward to that excursion as I fell asleep. I had no idea of how much was to happen before that week came to an end.

Andrew was now spending practically all his time with Betty and completely neglecting Carlos. Marianne had arrived, and David, understandably, disappeared for a couple of days. I met the two of them one evening at Pepe Moreno's, the most popular discotheque in Marbella. I have always liked this particular disco, partly because of the great variety of people who go there, but also because of its atmosphere. The disc jockey sits in a console, surrounded by flashing lights and dials, as if he were piloting a spacecraft, and there is an imitation satellite suspended from the ceiling which shoots its lasers in all directions, turning the whole building into a giant kaleidoscope. As the rock booms out, luminescent panels glow in every wall, except one where silent movies are back-projected. It is the surrealist, psychedelic pleasure dome of some other planet in the undreamed-of future.

Marianne looked cute. She was wearing a very chic new dress which I presumed David had bought her. While he was fighting his way to the bar to get us some drinks, Marianne asked me about my trip to Brazil and the carnival celebrations. She had a faraway look in her eyes, and nodded politely at my answers, but without any evident concentration. Leaning across the tiny cocktail table, where we were ensconced, I let my hand brush against the bare flesh of her arm, and I saw her tremble slightly.

Looking around furtively to ensure that David was still out of earshot, she murmured, 'David was not the only person I hoped to see when I agreed to come to Marbella.'

'Why don't you come over to my place when David is busy?' I invited. 'I am sure that we could find some way of passing the time, and you might enjoy the change.'

'I don't suppose he will mind, and anyway I am not his property. It's not as though we were married.'

Our gallant escort wormed his way through the press of bodies on the floor, and reached our table with most of our drinks unspilled. As he sat down, Marianne enquired casually what he was doing the next day.

'That's up to you, darling,' he replied. 'What would you like to do?'

'I thought that you said that you had some business to deal with.'

'That's all right,' David smiled. 'It can wait.'

'No, dear, I don't want to upset your arrangements.' Marianne's consideration was touching. 'You get on with whatever you have to do, and I'll look in on Xaviera.'

David shot a dirty look in my direction, and told Marianne that he was sure that I had so many things to attend to that I ought not to be bothered by having her descend on me. I assured him that I would be delighted to help him out. Reluctantly, he assented.

'We'll have all the rest of the time together,' said Marianne soothingly. 'And didn't you say that the day after tomorrow there was this very special party to which we have been invited?'

David nodded. The party at Daniël's villa was a sore subject with me. A formal invitation had been extended to David and Marianne, as his recognized partner, and a separate one to me alone. When I asked Daniël if I could bring along my girlfriend, he had informed me frigidly that it was not that sort of party. However, in the light of Betty's subsequent conduct, this slight no longer mattered, but I still resented it. After all, if Betty had been given the cold shoulder, I had received, figuratively speaking, a slap in the face.

As we left Pepe Moreno's, I squeezed David's arm.

'I thought that you were the man who was never jealous.'

'Not of another man, but a woman is a new kind of competition. You will leave something for me, won't you?' he added with a wistful grin.

'Of course, darling,' I chuckled. 'She will be returned to you, safe and sound, and probably all the better for the experience.'

Marianne and I spent most of the following afternoon in bed. We fed each other with a delicious fruit salad, mixed with honey, which I had prepared, but the love we made was sweeter than the food. It was her first time with a woman, and she reclined with a sensuous smile on her lips, and passively accepted my advances. Her skin was petal soft, and as smooth as the shiny silk of the dress which she had worn the night before. Everything about her was girlish, from her proud, pert breasts to the pretty little lips of her cunt, into which I slipped a soft, juicy piece of ripe mango. She was surprised, but curled up contentedly, like a well-fed cat, when I sucked it out again. The taste was of cold fruit and hot woman. Her nipples stood erect as I kissed her sensual mouth and masturbated against the top of her thighs. Her orgasm came quickly, and we both enjoyed two more before taking a rest, during which she told me that she had read the French translation of *The Happy Hooker*, in which a description of a poolside seduction by me of a redheaded woman had awakened lesbian fantasies in her for the first time.

'Wouldn't you have liked us to have had a threesome with David?' I asked.

She shook her head. Despite her liberated talk, she was still very inexperienced with men; perhaps she had been with six lovers altogether, and she was far too shy to indulge in anything as adventurous as group sex. However, she was an adorable young thing.

During these few days, my patience was strained to breaking point by Betty, who now only appeared in the apartment to change her clothes and take a bath. I told her that it was as though I were running a hotel without any guests, and that she was taking unfair advantage of my hospitality, but I might just as well have saved my breath. I had kept in touch with Carlos, who had witnessed the way Andrew and Betty were cavorting about, and who was grievously hurt. Andrew was, if anything, more spellbound than ever by Betty, after his humiliation by her and Grete, and he had no time at all for Carlos, or for anybody else.

Another disappointment was awaiting me in my treatment at Daniël's much-heralded reception. David had summed up the situation as Joëlle's bid to buy acceptance by Marbella 'society'. There were plenty of people who sneered at Daniël behind his back as a Jewish upstart, but were envious of his wealth. They would be quite ready, however, to eat his caviare and drink his champagne. Joëlle would exult in their presence at the villa, Daniël would get cynical amusement at their hypocrisy, and they would be superbly wined and dined. So everybody would be satisfied.

The villa had been completely redecorated and refurnished for the occasion, but there were the usual Andalucian problems. The electricians never showed up, so the lighting was not functioning. When that got fixed, the barmen were missing. Of the hundred and thirty people who had been invited, only a hundred and ninety were able to make it. When the first fifty guests were assembled, Joëlle was still in her bedroom, fixing her dress and make-up, much to the annoyance of Daniël, who kept sending for her. I suggested to David that she was probably getting laid, but when she did ultimately put in an appearance, her aloof manner led me to term her 'the hostess with the leastest'.

Nevertheless, the champagne was flowing liberally, and so was the gossip. Most of the people at our table were dreadful bores, but I found one really amusing character. He was a forty-year-old Dane who delighted to clown about and ridicule the more formal guests. He had a long flowing mane of golden hair, and disconcerted his more conservative neighbours by declaiming poetry in a resonant tenor. He wore a fanciful, Russian-style outfit, with a richly embroidered shirt with puffy sleeves and heavy red boots. When the band played some Russian music, he executed a lively Cossack dance, squatting back on his haunches with his arms folded. Such was his exuberance that there was a definite thaw, and his performance was greeted by a burst of applause. He was drunk, but pleasantly so, without any trace of aggression. Strangely enough, when I got to talk with him I became aware that he was actually a very shy person and his extrovert display was an elaborate act.

Despite this diversion, I was not unhappy when the

time came to leave, and I could not help contrasting the pretentiousness and artificiality of that evening with the simple, genuine good nature of the *feria* in Benahavis.

The following afternoon, I had a fateful conversation with Carlos. I had previously told him that, in my opinion, Andrew was an ungrateful, unfeeling wretch, and that Carlos would be well rid of him. He should pack Andrew's things in a suitcase and throw him out. Carlos had been so depressed that I was resolved to try and straighten him out, even though it meant that he would be obliged to face up to the unwelcome facts of his situation.

He had been drinking again, but was perfectly lucid. He wanted to know what Andrew had told me about him. I decided to be harsh: maybe my cruelty would achieve the necessary strengthening of Carlos's will for him to make the break with his obsessive parasite.

'He said that you were repulsively ugly and perpetually drunk,' I replied. 'He told me everything, except the truth.'

Carlos was silent for several seconds. Then he spoke in a voice broken with sadness and emotion.

'You are right, this can't go on. Tonight I shall pack his case and be rid of him for ever. And to think that it has come to this, because of your damned girlfriend! What does she want with a man, anyway?'

I said nothing, and after a short pause Carlos went on.

'I suppose I am not being fair to her. If it had not been her, there would have been somebody else. It was bound to happen, sooner or later. But I never thought it would be with a woman.'

'Well, at least you won't have to go on paying his bills,' I said, by way of consolation. 'I am sure that you will be able to find a kinder and more considerate companion, once he is out of the way. And I don't suppose that you

197

have been having much of a sex life with him for some time, have you?'

Carlos laughed grimly. 'I've had to get used to doing without it, although sometimes when he was asleep I would simply lie there, looking at him, and masturbate.'

He needed to talk – about anything. I listened while he described how he had gipsy blood on his mother's side and how superstitious she had been. She had been told by a fortune-teller that she would die within a year, and six months later she suffered a fatal heart attack. This event had deeply impressed Carlos, and the memory of that sinister clairvoyant seemed still to haunt him. But before he hung up, I thought that he was showing a new determination. He said that he would go to a hypnotist to try and get off the booze. This was going to be the biggest day of his life, he told me, and he was going to take a couple of Valium tablets to steady his nerves for what he had to do.

I called him next morning, but there was no answer. I tried again later with the same result, and I had an intuition that something terrible had happened. I ran out to the car, and drove straight over to his house.

I was shocked to find the place infested with policemen, perhaps a dozen of them, in the garden, on the terrace, in the house itself. Then I froze in horror. I saw Carlos's corpse, lying in the garden, only partly covered by a white sheet.

He had done exactly what he had promised, packing all Andrew's things carefully and neatly into a suitcase. Then he went into the garage and switched on the engine of his car. He attached a length of plastic hose to the exhaust and passed the end through the car window. He closed the garage door and sat in the driving seat, breathing in the poisonous fumes. An autopsy revealed that he had indeed taken some Valium – about twenty tablets!

I stood there, motionless and unable to speak. Then I began to cry softly. A few minutes later, Andrew arrived with Betty. They had no idea of what had happened, and the police took Andrew aside and talked with him. Betty's face was expressionless: I wondered what was going through her mind, behind that mask. Andrew shook his head wearily and spoke to her.

'I am sorry, but it looks as if I shall have to spend the whole afternoon with the police. They want to ask me a lot of questions. Christ, what a bloody mess! Why the hell did he have to do this?'

I turned on him, a cold fury surging through my brain. His callous indifference maddened me.

'Don't you think that it was you and your stupid selfishness that drove him to kill himself?'

Andrew rounded on me. 'What about you, Xaviera? Day after day, you have been playing the psychologist, pestering and probing. We understood each other; it was your mindfucking interference which destroyed our relationship.'

'Relationship? What sort of relationship do you think you had? You treated him like a dog.'

'That may be the way it looked to you,' Andrew retorted, 'but I knew what he needed. You tried to force him to play a role for which he was too feeble. You are the one who ought to have a bad conscience.'

Thinking back to that awful morning, I guess that probably we both felt guilty, in our own way. The police interrupted our bickering. They had found a note, addressed to me, in Carlos's handwriting. I read it aloud.

'"Nobody is to blame for what I have done, except myself. I knew that I was too weak to cope, with nowhere to go and with nobody to give me the love I need. The old fortune-teller who had predicted my mother's death had also warned me that I would die before September. Today has to be the day. Carlos."'

I turned away and drove back to my apartment.

Next day, Joseph picked me up to take me to his home in the mountains. I desperately needed to get away, and could hardly wait for his arrival. At last I would be able to obtain some relief from the grief and tension, and find comfort in the company of a sane, well-balanced and caring family.

The house itself was even more extraordinary than Joseph had led me to anticipate. It was so utterly isolated, surrounded by rolling grasslands and the forbidding, barren slopes of the steep mountains, that I felt that I had withdrawn from the outside world, into a sort of Andalucian Shangri-La. The weathered stone walls breathed tranquillity, and Joseph's paintings – big, bold canvases, which in some cases covered a whole wall – harmonized unexpectedly with the rough, local country-style furniture. Doors from old churches had been converted into massive tables, which stood on the stone-flagged floors of the great barn of a kitchen and the oddly shaped dining room which lay in the centre of the sprawling building. Having been forewarned by Joseph, I was not surprised by the number and variety of wildlife which regarded the house as being as much its property as Joseph's. It was somehow reassuring to see the fox sharing its quarters with a whole company of dogs of mixed and uncertain parentage, with no more hostility than that shown by the quartet of very independent-minded cats, whose home was the kitchen. But if the dogs were rag, tag and bobtail mongrels, the horses were very different, pure-blooded Arabs, a whole dozen of them. I stroked their glossy flanks, and they tossed their heads haughtily, aware of heir aristocratic superiority to all their neighbours.

In fact, for sheer majesty, the horses had a rival. Strutting over the grass came a string of peacocks, stepping daintily as if they disdained coming into contact with he earth, and fanning out the plumage of their tails to delight, dazzle and overawe mere men and women. The only jarring note was sounded by the crippled owl, a monster of a bird, which huddled at the back of the windowless barn, where it would hiss and screech at any stranger who dared to intrude. I peeped in at it, and it glared back at me with its huge, cold, unblinking eyes, before screaming its displeasure at my presence. I guess that even in the animal kingdom there are some who are born loners and value their isolation, so I respected the owl's desire for privacy, and returned to the more sociable inhabitants.

I was given a warm welcome by Ruth, a woman who exuded kindliness and common sense. She was not particularly pretty, but her features had about them a friendliness which was captivating. She was artistic, although far more down to earth than her temperamental husband. It was due to Ruth, I am sure, that the household functioned with such easy good humour: I found that the untroubled calm was the perfect remedy for my depressed state of mind and nervous tension.

They were a happy family, content to live their own life, up in the hills, and rarely bothering to come down to the bright lights of the coast. During the last two or three years Joseph had become fascinated by tennis, and he would entertain a number of other Americans who lived near Marbella, and who not only shared his enthusiasm for the game, but also his aversion to the crowded beaches and the tourist resorts. Joseph was a great host, leaving me free to wander around the grounds until I showed up, back at the house. He was constantly on the move: energy seemed to bubble out of him, and during the afternoon we played some pretty exhausting sets of tennis. What with that, swimming in the pool, and cantering across the grassy plain and up into the wooded hills on one of his fleet-footed horses, I was a new woman by the evening, and beginning to see the tragedy of Carlos is some sort of perspective. Over a simple supper, we talked about it, and Joseph passed a judgement which was probably as near the truth as anyone could attain.

'It sounds to me as if all three of you, Andrew, Betty and you, Xaviera, played a part in his tragedy, and yet no one of you was actually to blame for what happened. This man, Carlos, must have been mentally sick, on the brink as it were, and you chanced to be the ones who gave him that final push. But a man in that state of mind had not got the capacity to survive. If it had not occurred yesterday, it would have come sooner or later, whenever the next crisis arose, only then it would have been somebody else who gave the last little shove, the last turn of the screw which would have brought him beyond breaking point.'

And so, during that weekend, I came to terms with myself, chatting with Ruth and Joseph about life and art, sex and politics. I helped them pick tomatoes and pull onions and green peppers, and I sat in Joseph's enormous studio, lined with his paintings – he assured me that he always kept the best ones for his own home – and watched him paint with incredible speed and fluency.

The time for me to leave Spain was drawing near. I felt that I had got to know something of this country of such violent contrasts, and to appreciate the speed with which conditions changed after the death of Franco in 1975. In my own way, I had played some part in spreading more beral ideas and a freer way of life. I had argued for nude eaches, and I claim the credit for introducing the monoini to this part of the country. My books, previously anned, were now on sale openly.

There were some ludicrous moments. In Marbella, the police learned to look the other way when girls sunbathed opless, but I was informed that the practice was only olerated as long as they lay still and did not move. 'You an bake 'em, but not shake 'em,' I commented. But at nore or less the same time, the police swooped on about ifty nude sunbathers in Ibiza, who were condemned for outraging public morality'. I was more encouraged by the news that Spain had leaped into the vanguard of social eform by becoming the first country in the world to permit prisoners in jails to have sexual intercourse; only with their legally wedded wives, of course. I suppose that s what is meant by penal reform! What would Spain have n store for me when I returned the next year?

19

Ibiza Stopover

I had been told that Ibiza was a fabulous place, quite different from Marbella, and on my way back to Amsterdam, I was suddenly presented with the opportunity to visit the island. I had driven as far as Barcelona, where I chanced to meet Frans, a handsome Dutch boy who had lived with me for a couple of months in Holland. I was not pressed for time, so when he suggested that we take the ferry over to Ibiza, I readily agreed.

Frans was tall, with a broad-shouldered, muscular body, fair complexion and strong, regular features beneath a fine crop of curly golden hair. He was in his mid-twenties, and divorced after a brief, unhappy marriage. He was great fun, and a highly skilled and well-endowed lover. However, there were two flaws to his character which had led to our breaking up, and my showing him the door. Frans liked to drink, but he just could not handle booze, and when he was well tanked up he tended to become argumentative or downright aggressive. Less serious, perhaps, was his tendency to live in a fantasy world where he was always engaged in some bold commercial coup. I recall his campaign to manufacture plastic ploughs in India which, in more senses than one, never got off the ground, and his attempt to start a chain of farms to breed pedigree rabbits throughout the famine-stricken areas of Africa was, so to speak, equally ill-conceived. I got fed up with these fanciful projects, and I was not surprised to find that he was now once more enthusiastically tackling the more poverty-stricken markets of the dark continent, which he hoped would welome bulk exports of expensive Dutch and German beer. However, I reckoned that for the duration of a brief holiday I would be able to put up with these shortcomings, and I was influenced by the fact that, although not an outstanding linguist, he had a very talented tongue.

My first impression of Ibiza, as we approached it from the sea, was of lush green pastures amid ranges of steep hills from which narrow paths led down to the golden beaches which encircled the island. The weather was idyllic, and after a hasty exploration we rented a two-roomed apartment near Santa Eulalia, about fourteen kilometres outside Ibiza town.

Santa Eulalia itself consisted almost entirely of a main street and two or three parallel side streets on each side of it. In the country which surrounded the town there were many run-down farmhouses with no electricity and only cold water, and where telephones were an unheard-of luxury. These isolated buildings were owned or rented by the artistic colony, of whom some were genuine painters or sculptors. They were older and better dressed than the hippies and boppers of Ibiza town, as I was to discover later, and they were an altogether more entertaining set of people who seemed to enjoy a sense of togetherness derived from their primitive living conditions, which they showed when, like a group of shipwrecked seamen, they descended on the town to buy provisions and arrange barbecues.

The social centre of Santa Eulalia was Sandy's Bar, and there I met a bewildering variety of personalities. One of the first was Tim, an American in his mid-forties, who made a point of always appearing in cowboy costume. His immense Mexican hat added emphasis to his big, black, drooping moustache. He had recently suffered a severe heart attack, and he was now always accompanied by his eighteen-year-old son, who chauffeured his father in their Range Rover. His Hawaian wife usually stayed at home, Tim preferring the company of his mistress, a tall, willowy, former Miss Somewhere, whose bored expression proclaimed her awareness of her sex appeal and Tim's obligation to pay heavily for the privilege of her company.

Dave was an altogether more sympathetic character. A lanky American of Swedish descent, he was super-blond with a fine shock of unkempt hair, and he sported a bushy red moustache. I also preferred his style of dressing: white shirts and baggy trousers, which suited him. He had keen blue eyes and nothing seemed to escape them. He surely noticed me and when I vanished with him for a couple of hours, Frans became dreadfully anxious and frustrated. However, on that occasion, he had no real grounds for suspicion. Dave was a sculptor, and he took me to his studio where he showed me his sculptures, not his etchings. In the field in front of his house there was a group of six giant white eggs and a batch of oversized mushrooms, all examples of his work. My favourite, however, was a stone phallus, the top of which he had painted red and blue, and which reached up to his shoulder when I photographed him standing beside it. I thought that this picture of a man holding his cock would be a worthy addition to my collection. At Easter, Dave placed one of his giant stone eggs in the branches of a tree in the middle of his village. It was unanimously acclaimed as Easter egg of the year.

During my three-week stay in Ibiza, Dave and I made love several times. He had a terrific rhythm, and his cock was so long there were times when I thought that it would emerge from my throat. It appealed to my sense of humour that when we made love on the grass, lying between his huge eggs, about a dozen real chickens would pick their way around us, unperturbed by our conduct.

Maybe it was love among the chickens which had been the inspiration for his statues.

While I was wandering further afield, making love, Frans had settled down to doing a round of the bars. About a week after our arrival, in Sandy's Bar we came across Grant, a tiny Jewish guy from the Bronx, and his two sons. The elder, a handsome seventeen-year-old lad, was sexy, but had a nasty, sarcastic manner, and I preferred his brother, who was altogether a more witty and kind person. Grant confided in me that the boy, who was just fifteen, was an avid fan of mine and badly needed to find a good sexual partner. His remark did not fall on deaf ears.

So one morning when Frans had gone off on one of his habitual drinking bouts, I went over to Grant's house and visited my admirer. His father greeted me like an old friend, but shortly afterwards found an excuse to go out shopping. As his brother was not at home, the kid and I were alone together. He was excited, but as nervous as an actor suffering from stage fright on an opening night. I kissed him on the lips, and noticed that he was blushing. I asked him to take me to his own room, and once inside, I took off his shorts. I made the action really sexy, moving slowly and hesitating for a moment, before the last sudden, unexpected tug revealed his bare buttocks. I found myself facing a really very nice cock, almost as long as Dave's and, to my pleasant surprise, twice as thick. It would be a pity to leave this virgin territory for some young girl to be the first to explore, I considered.

I pulled off my dress and we lay naked on the bed. I let him cradle his head against my chest. He had told me that he had a fantasy of having his head crushed between the full, heavy breasts of an older woman. I guess that since his father was a rather immature person who had been divorced for years and had no steady girlfriend, the boy lacked a mother figure. He also adored playing at wrestling, and it was quite a turn-on as our nude bodies rubbed against each other. He was very horny and the flagstaff of his penis kept getting in the way, so I punished it with a friendly but quite sharp slap, which he loved. When I let him pin me down and sit astride me, my penance was to kiss his beautiful cock. Then I placed it between my tits, and licked and sucked across them alternately.

At last I decided that the time had come for a more adult pastime, and we made love tenderly and sensually. I brought him quickly to a climax between my tits, and he shot a great fountain of thick sperm into the air and all over my face and my hair. A few minutes sufficed for him to regain his erection, and this time I allowed him to penetrate me, which he had been craving to do, and after some twenty strokes, he came again. He was breathing hard and sweat was running down his hairless chest, but he was a very happy and fulfilled boy. I had been concentrating so much on the pleasure that I wanted to give this virgin boy that I never had an orgasm myself, and yet it was an unforgettable experience which I enjoyed enormously.

When I got back to our apartment Frans was waiting for me, and in a very suspicious frame of mind, but I managed to divert him by challenging him to a game of tennis. We joined another couple, but since Frans had confined himself to a strictly liquid diet, his play was so erratic that our partners sent him off the court. He claimed that he was seeing four balls, a sort of double double vision!

Later that day, we were back in Sandy's Bar when Grant and his boys came in. My protégé ran over and gave me a big hug and a kiss, while his proud father congratulated me, in a voice which everybody could hear, on the excellent job I had done on his boy. He declared that every father should be so lucky as to be able to call on me to take care of his son and pop his cherry.

Now when he was drunk, Frans became truculent and downright violent, and this was the last straw. He was insanely jealous and started to shake me with the strength of an enraged animal. I thought that he was going to hurl me through the glass door, but instead, in his drunken fury, he kicked the door, smashing the glass, and stepped through the wreckage on to the patio, scattering thousands of fragments through the bar. He seized me again and tried to thrust my shoulder against the jagged broken door, but he was grabbed and overpowered by the other customers. In the mêlée he had gashed his leg badly, cutting into a vein in two places. The pain sobered him up, and he was as gentle as a lamb when he was rushed off to hospital.

We had by now found another apartment, closer to the centre of town, and I had the task of manhandling the incapacitated Frans into our new abode. Fortunately, I was helped by another new friend, Eli, a Russian Jewish painter from Glasgow, who moved in with us.

All the regulars of Sandy's Bar were colourful, flamboyant people, but there was one man who dominated them all. He was a Dutchman called Adler, and he lived up to his name, for he was an eagle to whom the lesser birds, mere painters and sculptors, deferred. They called him the King of Ibiza, and one thing was for sure – he was very, very rich. Rumour had it that he had made a fortune dealing in hash, and Adler never bothered to deny it. He was fair and sinewy, and had the piercing blue eyes of a shrewd, tough businessman.

Whatever may have been the shadier aspects of his

past, Adler now was involved in all sorts of respectable enterprises, owning discotheques and substantial chunks of real estate. In fact, wherever you looked, Adler had a finger in the pie. Currently, he was investing in skating rinks. He was accustomed to taking business decisions with a cold, unemotional precision, and he showed the same hardness in his personal relationships. No woman could boast of being his girlfriend for more than a week, and his refusal to become involved endowed him with an aura of being unattainable, which fascinated the girls. And he possessed the trappings of great wealth: an immense estate, with every imaginable luxury and a vast entourage of servants and hangers-on, who catered for all his whims. His 36-metre sailing ship was an awesome sight, riding at anchor and overshadowing all the other yachts in the harbour.

Actually, there was a softer side to the stone-hearted tycoon, and he was capable of great generosity, especially to his women companions, whom he treated with perfect courtesy and consideration during his brief encounters. Eli had benefited from this aspect of his character because Adler had become a patron of the arts, and he had bought a whole collection of Eli's paintings, without demeaning himself by bargaining over price. This was quite a break for Eli, whom I considered to be a talented artist, but who, after fifteen years in Ibiza, was still waiting to be recognized. His studio was stacked with hundreds of unsold paintings.

I also collected a few of Eli's works, although on a rather different basis. The first canvas was acquired as a barter deal, in lieu of payment by Eli for bed and board. Another was a birthday present, but I paid him a hundred dollars for the third.

Eli, a quiet intellectual, had been shy and sexually

rustrated up to a couple of years previously. The reason was that he was never known to smile, not because of a miserable trait in his character, but due to his having ghastly teeth, and he lacked the money and the courage to get them fixed. Then he met a wealthy American who took a liking to his paintings and bought some. It turned out that he was a dentist, and so Eli carried out another barter deal, and with his dazzling new false teeth, he found himself the smiling centre of attraction for a whole bevy of beautiful girls.

With Frans confined to his bed, I took advantage of the location of our new apartment to get into town and inspect the local talent. Ibiza was crowded and noisy, but a very attractive place, at least at first glance. Seated on the terrace of the Montesol, I surveyed the scene. There were some gorgeous blondes, and many of the men were handsome, suntanned specimens. But I soon came to the conclusion that this beauty was skin-deep.

Everybody seemed to parade up and down the street at least four times, each one pursuing his or her own private dream. The average age was somewhere between fifteen and twenty-five; I was beginning to wonder whether I would qualify as a senior citizen. I tried chatting to some of the kids, most of whom had very ordinary jobs back home – shop assistants, hairdressers and office workers – and for them, Ibiza was the glamorous island where their illusions became reality. Unlike their elders in Santa Eulalia, they had little conversation, other than which celebrity they had spied in the Pasha discotheque or on the beach at Salinas. I overheard a lovely Indonesian girl telling her equally attractive blonde companion how Ursula Andress had been at the disco, but it was the handsome disc jockey who had been the star of the show for her. He had promised to take her home when the disco closed, but waiting outside the stage door she discovered four other girls he had dated. I never did hear the end of the story, since she was interrupted by the arrival of a wildly pretty boy, who greeted her enthusiastically, kissing her and hugging her as if she were the fairy princess for whom he had been waiting all his life. I was intrigued by this new turn of events, for the boy was fantastically attired in a purple jacket, with an array of chains and bracelets, and his eyes were carefully made up with a little kohl, the whole tastefully crowned by his pink and green dyed hair.

The girl clearly doted on him and gazed at him enraptured while he devoured a club sandwich and a fancy cocktail, which he ordered in a loud, affected voice. I noticed that he never offered either of the girls anything, but the Indonesian beauty was happy enough to be breathing the same air as this precious creature. As he finished his food, another good-looking boy, tall and blond, perhaps a German or Scandinavian, came up and started talking to him. In no time at all the girls were forgotten, and the two of them strolled off together, arm in arm. The young gentleman did not bother with the formality of paying his bill, but left that detail to his female admirer.

When I asked some of the men what the action was like, they shook their heads despondently. A lot of the chicks were couples who took a small room and who were not interested in fucking, but they would follow guys with money or dope – or preferably both. Even then, when it came to bedtime, they usually disappeared; they were great cock teasers. I found that there was a group of hookers from Hamburg in town, but they were hopefully seeking some wealthy older men who could be enticed into marriage.

212

It was the same story on the beaches, where the lovelies would saunter about in their diminutive G-strings and . . . thigh-length boots! The beaches were surrounded by sand dunes; great voyeur country as I was to discover. One morning, I was on the beach with Dave. We were gently rubbing each other and his cock swelled up tremendously. Hearing a rustling sound, I got to my feet, and saw a Spanish man lying among the dunes watching us and masturbating.

There were other people who were also busy watching the personalities of Ibiza. There were all kinds of dubious types hanging around, Germans with war records, dope peddlers, American drop-outs, and every now and then somebody would draw too much attention to himself and disappear. All the boats were under constant surveillance, and one day a party of us were guests on Adler's boat, when he got fed up with the attentions of a dozen uniformed and plain-clothes police, along with a fraternal delegation from Interpol. He spotted a man he knew to be a Japanese undercover agent pretending to be an innocent tourist, pointing his camera at us. Adler ordered his crew and his more questionable cronies below, and had all the pretty girls on board pose at the rail. There must have been some horny spies that day!

All this time Frans was recuperating, and we had long got over our dispute. He was a friendly guy and good company, as long as he kept off the booze. His right leg was still bandaged from toe to thigh, and our love-making took on a new and kinkier dimension. As he was immobile, I had become his messenger from the outside world, and he would sit and listen attentively when I brought home the local gossip. He was greatly amused by my descriptions of the wildlife of the island: the only topic he did not want to hear about was my sexual skirmishes.

As I gazed at his helpless body with his white-covered leg resting on a pillow, I was reminded of a letter which I had received at *Penthouse* magazine, and which I related to him. A rather homely girl was quite neglected by the men at a ski resort, until she had an accident and was forced to lie in bed with her leg in a cast. Maybe it was her helplessness, but at once all the local Don Juans swarmed around her. Back home and fit again, she was once more ignored, until she had the idea of having a couple of casts made which she could slip on her arm or her leg before she went out. It worked, and with her cast on, she was never again cast off.

'Doesn't a bandage have the same effect on you, Xaviera?' Frans asked hopefully.

I had to admit that there was something appealing in his vulnerability, but I needed the skill of a professional contortionist to find a mutually satisfying position. Several times I sucked him, although there was nothing he could do for me. But, as he lay back in the bed, I would sometimes tantalize him by kneeling on the pillow, with my pussy just out of reach of his mouth, so that he could get a sniff of the fruit which was denied him. As he strained upwards, I would jerk away from his lips, and his movement, slight as it was, would send a stab of pain through his very tender leg. But I was not too cruel to my prematurely bedridden Romeo, and since I could find consolation elsewhere, I concentrated on satisfying his physical demands. When I played my lips and tongue up and down his rigid cock, performing on my mouth organ as I termed it, his tormented body twitched and writhed, and his mounting excitement turned me on in a funny way also. As the pace quickened, we would get clumsy, and I would bump against his crippled leg. It must have hurt a lot, since Frans would howl like a cat that had been hit by

214

well-aimed brick. I would tease him by pretending that was going to hit his leg, and he would cringe back, but s he was still aching to get his rocks off, he could not ear himself away, and he had to accept any pain which I nflicted on him, knowingly or not.

One day on the beach I met Julia, an ex-lover of mine rom Amsterdam. She was quite a cinema enthusiast, and here had been a wild session one year when I went with ter to the Berlin Film Festival. She had great tits, but vhat I remembered most vividly was her heavy, mmensely strong legs, which almost squeezed the life out of me when I was sucking her. Julia was a full-bodied voman; she possessed the sort of figure which Rubens vould have been proud to paint. I had enjoyed quite a ew threesomes with Julia and her husband, although he vas inclined to sit back and watch us while he masturbated, leaving the energetic stuff to the women. Usually Julia would cruise for young girls; I was perhaps the only exception to the rule. What I loved was to suck on the :hick, succulent lips of her cunt; she had possibly the meatiest pussy on which I had ever fed. And her clitoris was a fine, outstanding member which insisted on receiving my full attention. She was a lovely, plump woman and absolutely oozed femininity, the sort who make my mouth water merely at the thought of the warm welcome awaiting me between their seductive thighs.

However, outside the privacy of their bedroom, the two of them were pillars of bourgeois respectability, and they would have died rather than let their prudish friends and neighbours catch a whiff of the scandalous goings on between their lily-white sheets.

We went for a stroll along the almost deserted beach, and I casually put my arm around her shoulders. It chanced to touch her tit, and her nipple immediately stiffened.

But Julia suddenly recoiled in alarm and pointed, saying, 'Look, over there! That man, standing by the rocks. He was masturbating, here, in front of everybody. God, how disgusting!'

He was facing out to sea, but he kept turning round to watch us. When he did so, his cock, firmly gripped in his right hand, was clearly visible. And I definitely approved of what I glimpsed, really hefty, a winner if ever I saw one! But Julia was shocked and turned to run away.

I grabbed her arm. 'What's the matter with you? We lie around, stark naked, on the beach and Madam Puritan gets hysterical at the sight of one guy jerking off. Now, just you stand still, and watch this.'

I walked over to where the man was standing. As I approached, he tried to push his cock back inside his trunks, but that was difficult because of his mammoth erection. He turned his head away, perhaps in shame, or maybe he was afraid that I would denounce him to the police. But I called out to him, in my best Spanish, that I wanted to suck his cock. He was flabbergasted, but as soon as he realized that this was for real, he waved towards Julia, and made it clear that he would like a threesome with my big-boobed companion. He wanted to lead us discreetly into the bushes behind the sand dunes, but I informed him that she was not playing, and he could have it with me alone, there where we were standing, in full view on the beach, or not at all.

It did not take him a moment to make up his mind and accept my proposition on my terms. His big cock had a salty flavour, presumably from the sea, and I was having a fine, tasty meal, when he suddenly pulled away. Maybe he feared that the crazy, horny foreign woman wanted to

something worse to him than hand him over to the
cal cops. I burst out laughing, but after a brief pause,
e were back in business. At the very moment when he
ame, I pulled his cock out of my mouth and turned it so
at Julia got a perfect view of the thick stream of sperm
ushing over my hands. She was standing open-mouthed
nd unable to believe her eyes, but she was rubbing
erself between her legs under her wrap-around dress.

Having dismissed our exhibitionist, I was ready to
esume our leisurely walk, but there was another unex-
ected diversion. While I had been fully occupied, a
oung fair-haired man, absolutely naked apart from a
raw Ibizenko basket which hung from his shoulders, had
alked up to where we were putting on our live show.
rom the condition of his penis, it was obvious that he
ad witnessed everything, and enjoyed it. Beside him was
nother young man, his lover I would guess. But the
ewcomer was ready for a swap of partners, and he
rinned at me through pearly white teeth and congratu-
ated me.

'That really looked great. How about giving me the
ame treatment?'

Julia was on the verge of hysterics, but I was more than
eady to oblige. She could not believe that I would indulge
ny fantasies to the extent of doing it again in public,
where at any time we could be surprised by the police and
hrown into jail.

So for the second time within half an hour, I was down
n my knees: I must have been the most game blower in
he whole of Spain. This cock was circumcised, and much
inker than the previous tenant of my mouth. The guy
vas pretty worked up before we started and with only
alf a dozen thrusts, he was ready to come. He wanted to
nish in my mouth, but I smiled at Julia and told him that

217

I wanted some fun as well. So I placed him between m
tits and rubbed my pussy against his leg, as his whit
cream streamed all over my breasts. By now, Julia wa
openly masturbating, but without removing her sarong.

She had played a prominent part in the women'
movement back in Holland, and I felt that I had don
something to broaden her outlook by giving her a dem
onstration of liberated behaviour.

And so back to Frans. I took a quick bath, and then w
had the hottest sex we had enjoyed for a long time, an
he still does not know the cause of that burst o
hyperactivity.

The time seemed to fly. Within a few days, Frans wa
moving about again and our stopover in Ibiza drew to
close. The beautiful people were more beautiful than eve
– and more boring.

The day before we left, Frans, at last without hi
bandages, was sitting with me on the beach, both of u
naked, when a group of the Guardia Civil, in full uniform
emerged from the bushes and arrested the nearest nud
sunbathers. They must have taken about twenty tourists
but by then the rest of us had made ourselves scarce, o
grabbed a G-string or bikini to hide our shame. S
paradise had not yet arrived!

However, my luck held and Spain has not joined th
ranks of those countries which have closed their door
to me.

And so I still have my place in the sun where I ca
welcome yet more of those Knights in the Gardens o
Spain. Maybe I'll meet you there some day – or som
night.

Postscript

This all happened eleven years ago. In the meantime, there have been many changes, both in the Spain and the Brazil which I have described. And, as far as I am concerned, Spain is no longer the novelty which it used to be; it has become my home. So why have I taken this book off the shelf and revised it for publication?

I have related many of my subsequent adventures in later books, and I felt that the loyal followers of Xaviera have the right to be told this chapter of my life. After all, I must live up to my reputation as the writer who hides nothing. And rereading the manuscript, it was obvious to me that, whatever may take place in public life, the basic things remain. It takes more than a change of government to alter the way men and women make love.

So, I look back at these events with amusement and nostalgia, and I hope that you have as much fun reading about them as I had living them.

MARBELLA, 1986

A selection of sexology books in paperback
from Grafton Books

To order direct from the publisher just tick the titles you want
and fill in the order form.

GF3981

Bestsellers available in paperback from Grafton Books

Emmanuelle Arsan

Emmanuelle	£2.50	☐
Emmanuelle 2	£2.50	☐
Laure	£1.95	☐
Nea	£1.95	☐
Vanna	£2.50	☐

Jonathan Black

Ride the Golden Tiger	£2.95	☐
Oil	£2.50	☐
The World Rapers	£2.50	☐
The House on the Hill	£2.50	☐
Megacorp	£2.50	☐
The Plunderers	£2.50	☐

Herbert Kastle

Cross-Country	£2.50	☐
Little Love	£2.50	☐
Millionaires	£2.50	☐
Miami Golden Boy	£2.50	☐
The Movie Maker	£2.95	☐
The Gang	£2.50	☐
Hit Squad	£1.95	☐
Dirty Movies	£2.95	☐
Hot Prowl	£1.95	☐
Sunset People	£2.50	☐
David's War	£1.95	☐

Bestsellers available in paperback from Grafton Books

the publisher just tick the titles you want
form. **GF4282**

All these books are available at your local bookshop or newsagent, or can be ordered direct from the publisher.

To order direct from the publishers just tick the titles you want and fill in the form below.

Name _____

Address _____

_____

Send to:
Grafton Cash Sales
PO Box 11, Falmouth, Cornwall TR10 9EN.

Please enclose remittance to the value of the cover price plus:

UK 60p for the first book, 25p for the second book plus 15p per copy for each additional book ordered to a maximum charge of £1.90.

BFPO 60p for the first book, 25p for the second book plus 15p per copy for the next 7 books, thereafter 9p per book.

Overseas including Eire £1.25 for the first book, 75p for second book and 28p for each additional book.

_____

Grafton Books reserve the right to show new retail prices on covers, which may differ from those previously advertised in the text or elsewhere.